D1261920

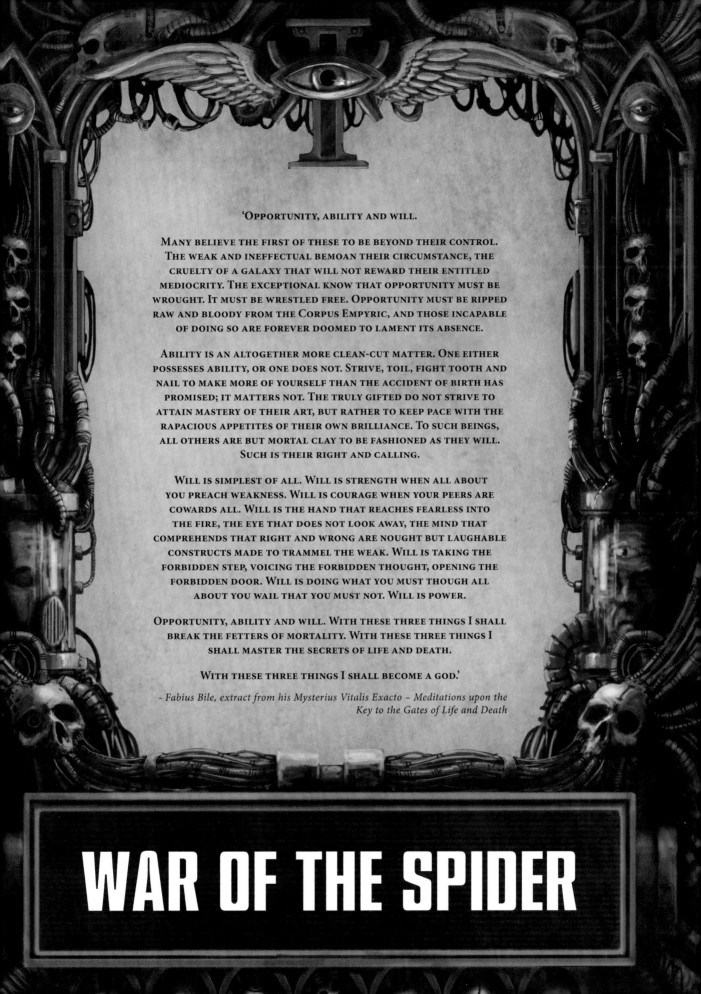

'OPPORTUNITY, ABILITY AND WILL.

MANY BELIEVE THE FIRST OF THESE TO BE BEYOND THEIR CONTROL.
THE WEAK AND INEFFECTUAL BEMOAN THEIR CIRCUMSTANCE, THE
CRUELTY OF A GALAXY THAT WILL NOT REWARD THEIR ENTITLED
MEDIOCRITY. THE EXCEPTIONAL KNOW THAT OPPORTUNITY MUST BE
WROUGHT. IT MUST BE WRESTLED FREE. OPPORTUNITY MUST BE RIPPED
RAW AND BLOODY FROM THE CORPUS EMPYRIC, AND THOSE INCAPABLE
OF DOING SO ARE FOREVER DOOMED TO LAMENT ITS ABSENCE.

ABILITY IS AN ALTOGETHER MORE CLEAN-CUT MATTER. ONE EITHER
POSSESSES ABILITY, OR ONE DOES NOT. STRIVE, TOIL, FIGHT TOOTH AND
NAIL TO MAKE MORE OF YOURSELF THAN THE ACCIDENT OF BIRTH HAS
PROMISED; IT MATTERS NOT. THE TRULY GIFTED DO NOT STRIVE TO
ATTAIN MASTERY OF THEIR ART, BUT RATHER TO KEEP PACE WITH THE
RAPACIOUS APPETITES OF THEIR OWN BRILLIANCE. TO SUCH BEINGS,
ALL OTHERS ARE BUT MORTAL CLAY TO BE FASHIONED AS THEY WILL.
SUCH IS THEIR RIGHT AND CALLING.

WILL IS SIMPLEST OF ALL. WILL IS STRENGTH WHEN ALL ABOUT
YOU PREACH WEAKNESS. WILL IS COURAGE WHEN YOUR PEERS ARE
COWARDS ALL. WILL IS THE HAND THAT REACHES FEARLESS INTO
THE FIRE, THE EYE THAT DOES NOT LOOK AWAY, THE MIND THAT
COMPREHENDS THAT RIGHT AND WRONG ARE NOUGHT BUT LAUGHABLE
CONSTRUCTS MADE TO TRAMMEL THE WEAK. WILL IS TAKING THE
FORBIDDEN STEP, VOICING THE FORBIDDEN THOUGHT, OPENING THE
FORBIDDEN DOOR. WILL IS DOING WHAT YOU MUST THOUGH ALL
ABOUT YOU WAIL THAT YOU MUST NOT. WILL IS POWER.

OPPORTUNITY, ABILITY AND WILL. WITH THESE THREE THINGS I SHALL
BREAK THE FETTERS OF MORTALITY. WITH THESE THREE THINGS I
SHALL MASTER THE SECRETS OF LIFE AND DEATH.

WITH THESE THREE THINGS I SHALL BECOME A GOD.'

*- Fabius Bile, extract from his Mysterius Vitalis Exacto – Meditations upon the
Key to the Gates of Life and Death*

WAR OF THE SPIDER

CONTENTS

PRODUCED BY THE WARHAMMER STUDIO

This book is dedicated to the memory of Geoff Robinson, 1985-2019.

With thanks to the Mournival and the Infinity Circuit for their additional playtesting services

INTRODUCTION

The Emperor's realm reels in the wake of the Great Rift's opening. Everywhere, madness and mutation run riot and Imperial armies fight desperate battles for survival against nightmarish odds. Chaos is in the ascendant, and in few locations is this more true than amidst the flames of War Zone Cadia.

Long did the fortress world of Cadia stand against the furious assault of Abaddon the Despoiler and his Thirteenth Black Crusade. Yet it could not stand forever, and Abaddon left Cadia a shattered and blasted husk. As he swept on towards fresh conquests, the warp interstice known as the Eye of Terror expanded in his wake. Day by day it swallows more of the region known as the Cadian Gate, and as the tendrils of the warp spread like blood through churning waters, one planetary system after another is beset by massed psychic mutation and plagues of madness.

The core of Abaddon's Black Crusade forces might have accompanied their master towards War Zone Vigilus, but teeming hordes of heretics, renegades, daemons and opportunistic xenos still prey upon the isolated Imperial enclaves that remain. Tides of anarchy and bloodshed sweep through War Zone Cadia, presenting to some a golden opportunity to further their own twisted agendas.

Fabius Bile is one such profiteer of misery. Emerging from his stronghold deep within the Eye of Terror, the Spider spins a new web of cruelty and perversion. Working through puppet warlords and experimental subjects, he has drawn in foes from both the Death Guard and the elite agents of the Imperium. He seeks to reap a nightmarish bio-harvest from these assembled enemies so as to further his latest malign schemes. Yet they are dangerous quarry indeed. Bile's forces are outnumbered, and he will require all of his wicked cunning if he is to emerge victorious from this war he has begun.

IN THIS BOOK

This book is part of Psychic Awakening, an ongoing series set in the aftermath of the Great Rift. It contains an overview from the perspectives of the Death Guard, the Imperial Agents and Fabius Bile.

Inside you will find:

- The story of Bile's cunning campaign of misdirection and atrocity against his Death Guard and Imperial enemies.
- Three missions to recreate the key engagements of the War of the Spider.
- Updated rules for the Adeptus Custodes, the Death Guard and for the Agents of Bile, including Relics, Stratagems and more.
- Updated datasheets for the Sisters of Silence, Imperial Assassins and, of course, Fabius Bile himself.

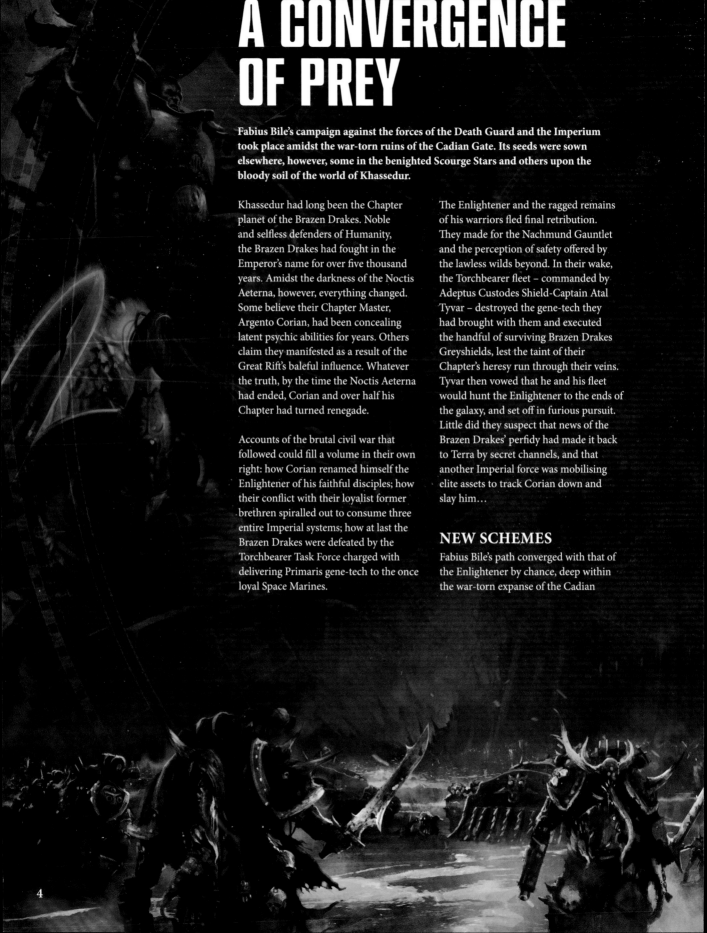

A CONVERGENCE OF PREY

Fabius Bile's campaign against the forces of the Death Guard and the Imperium took place amidst the war-torn ruins of the Cadian Gate. Its seeds were sown elsewhere, however, some in the benighted Scourge Stars and others upon the bloody soil of the world of Khassedur.

Khassedur had long been the Chapter planet of the Brazen Drakes. Noble and selfless defenders of Humanity, the Brazen Drakes had fought in the Emperor's name for over five thousand years. Amidst the darkness of the Noctis Aeterna, however, everything changed. Some believe their Chapter Master, Argento Corian, had been concealing latent psychic abilities for years. Others claim they manifested as a result of the Great Rift's baleful influence. Whatever the truth, by the time the Noctis Aeterna had ended, Corian and over half his Chapter had turned renegade.

Accounts of the brutal civil war that followed could fill a volume in their own right: how Corian renamed himself the Enlightener of his faithful disciples; how their conflict with their loyalist former brethren spiralled out to consume three entire Imperial systems; how at last the Brazen Drakes were defeated by the Torchbearer Task Force charged with delivering Primaris gene-tech to the once loyal Space Marines.

The Enlightener and the ragged remains of his warriors fled final retribution. They made for the Nachmund Gauntlet and the perception of safety offered by the lawless wilds beyond. In their wake, the Torchbearer fleet – commanded by Adeptus Custodes Shield-Captain Atal Tyvar – destroyed the gene-tech they had brought with them and executed the handful of surviving Brazen Drakes Greyshields, lest the taint of their Chapter's heresy run through their veins. Tyvar then vowed that he and his fleet would hunt the Enlightener to the ends of the galaxy, and set off in furious pursuit. Little did they suspect that news of the Brazen Drakes' perfidy had made it back to Terra by secret channels, and that another Imperial force was mobilising elite assets to track Corian down and slay him…

NEW SCHEMES

Fabius Bile's path converged with that of the Enlightener by chance, deep within the war-torn expanse of the Cadian

Gate. The Primogenitor was ever a master opportunist and soon turned happenstance to his advantage.

Bile was labouring in service to a grand new scheme, one he had conceived of even as the galaxy writhed with the opening of the Great Rift. Speculation was rife throughout the Eye of Terror and beyond as to what the Spider might be planning: another attempt at cloning or creating his own Primarch; the fashioning of some dread new altered army; development of a weapon that could lay low Roboute Guilliman or indeed any other similarly godlike being. Bile himself had revealed nothing of his schemes, even to his closest lieutenants, but he moved with a purpose through the mayhem and horror of the Imperium Nihilus.

That purpose had first manifested in the theft of a mighty arcane artefact that had originally been bestowed upon the Death Guard by none other than the Great Unclean One Rotigus himself. Named the Ark Cornucontagious, this gruesome gift of Nurgle seethed with a warp malady that triggered catastrophic and uncontrolled bodily regeneration in its victims. To the unnatural physiognomies of the Death Guard this was a boon, for the Ark's foul emissions allowed them to heal battle damage faster than their foes could inflict it. To any other being, however, the relic's effect was a monstrous blight that soon reduced even the mightiest warrior to a heaving mound of diseased flesh and ruptured, blubbery innards.

What uses Bile could have for such a perilous and revolting artefact was a secret he kept to himself. Regardless, at the head of a ragtag alliance of renegade warbands he had braved the perils of the newly conquered Scourge Stars and successfully made off with the Ark, safely swathing it within a potent stasis field. That campaign had cost Bile all but a handful of his followers, however. Now he fled back towards the Eye of Terror, through the roiling warp storms of the Imperium Nihilus, with Typhus himself at his heels.

Bile could not flee directly back to his lair in the Eye of Terror lest he bring the wrath of the Death Guard down upon it. He needed fresh allies who could help him dissuade his pursuers before he made good his escape. Fate, or perhaps the Dark Gods, sent him the Enlightener.

Argento Corian had not been idle since reaching War Zone Cadia. He had claimed the tainted fortress world of Dessah for his base and had reforged the Brazen Drakes into a warband calling themselves the Shriven, who now fought under the colours of Abaddon's Black Legion. Yet Corian had caught wind of the vengeful Imperial pursuit even now bearing down upon him. Thus, even as Bile saw in the Shriven an army he could turn against his pursuers, so they believed that with the Primogenitor's gifts they would be strong enough to crush the Imperial agents coming for their heads. It was a diabolical alliance of mutual mistrust, and one that Bile soon turned to his twisted advantage.

WAR ZONE CADIA

Abaddon's devastation of Cadia tore the keystone from the Imperial defences around the Eye of Terror. Even as those defences crumbled, the roiling energies of the warp rushed in through every gap. Much of the region is now feral and lawless, its sub-sectors carved up between warring heretic warbands while surviving Imperial worlds hold out amidst oceans of foes.

NAOGEDDON

DIMMAMAR

STORM OF THE EMPEROR'S WRATH

SEGMENTUM OBSCURUS

HALO STARS

CALIXIS SECTOR

FINIAL SECTOR

CYPRA MUNDI

VALHALLA

MORDIAN

THE EYE OF TERROR

VIGILUS

ALARIC

CADIA

BELIS CORONA

PISCINA

CHINCHARE

MOLOV

NECRON MEPHRIT DYNAS

AGRIPINAA

Nachmund Gauntlet

HYDRAPHUR

ARMAGEDDON

ELYSIA

CICATRIX MALEDICTUM

LASTRATI

SEGMENTUM SOLAR

GOLGOTHA

VORDRAST

SEGMENTUM PACIFICUS

TERRA & MARS

RYZA

THE MAELSTROM

CATACHAN

GATHALAMOR

NECROMUNDA

BADAB

MACHARIA

ULTIMA MACHARIA

KRIEG

LUTHER McINTYRE

TALLARN

NOCTURNE

BALOR

CHIROS

OPHELIA

UHULIS SECTOR

V'RUN

SIREN'S STORM

BANE'S LANDIN

ALEUSIS

RYNN'S WORLD

NEPHI SECTO

SOLSTICE

SEGMENTUM TEMPESTUS

REDUCTUS SECTOR

AGRAX

BAKKA

ANTAGONIS

GRYPHONNE IV

SAN LEOR

ILLUSTRIS

THE VEILED REGION

THE CADIAN GATE

TO NEMESIS TESSERA

CADIA

BELIS CORONA

AGRIPINAA

TO HYDRAPHUR

TO TERRA AND MARS

CADIAN SYSTEM

KASR PARTOX
(FORTRESS WORLD)

ST. JOSMANE'S HOPE
(MILITARY PRISON WORLD)

CADIA
(FORMER LYNCHPIN FORTRESS WORLD)

SOLAR MARIATUS
(FORTRESS WORLD)

KOROLIS
(PROMETHIAN PRODUCTION FACILITY)

PROSAN
(HOSTILE ENVIRONMENT TRAINING FACILITY)

VIGILATUM
(NAVAL TRAINING WORLD)

MACHARIA
(MILITARISED HIVE WORLD)

KASR SONNEN
(FORTRESS WORLD)

KASR HOLN
(FORTRESS WORLD)

BELIS CORONA SYSTEM

BAIRSTEN PRIME
(DURALIUM MINING WORLD)

LAURENTIX
(CONTACT LOST)

MALUSOIR
(DEATH WORLD)

BELISIMAR
(CLASSIFIED)

ANTAR
(FIRE WORLD)

BELIS CORONA
(NAVAL DOCK)

GELDARIS
(PURGED)

CORWYN BELT (RADIOACTIVE ASTEROID FIELD)

ULTIMA SEGMENTUM

FORMUND

SOMNIUM STARS

LE

KAR DUNIASH

CORINTHE

ATTILA

TEMPORARY RIFT CORRIDOR

IRILLO PRIME

THE YMGA MONOLITH

SCHINDELGHEIST

T'AU EMPIRE

NECRON SAUTEKH DYNASTY

HADEX ANOMALY

CHARADON SECTOR

ICHAR IV

THE SCOURGE STARS

MACRAGGE

BLACK REACH

RDUS

CRON ILAKH NASTY

FALSE HOPE

SALEM

AMIDST THE RUINS

Due to the catastrophic empyric emanations saturating the wider War Zone Cadia, it is tremendously difficult to take any accurate measure of the forces currently engaged there. The following represent partial strategic estimates by martial haruspexes and naval observers based on Belis Corona, and focus on elements involved in the campaign designated the War of the Spider.

DEATH GUARD FORCES

THE TRAVELLER'S HOST

The Harbingers .... 4 Vectoriums
The Inexorable ....1 Vectorium
The Ferrymen .... 2 Vectoriums
The Neverdead ....[Numbers unknown but vast]
Terminus Est [see sub-file 777] .... 1 Capital Ship
Plague Fleet .... 7 Warships

THE CULTS OF THE EYE

Cult of the Festering Touch ....1 Chaos Cult
Fraternity of Fecund Gifts ....1 Chaos Cult
The Weeping Ones ....1 Chaos Cult
The Rusted.......................................1 Chaos Cult
Cult of Delicious Misery....................1 Chaos Cult
Cult of the Putrefying Emperor........1 Chaos Cult
Worshippers of the Rotted Stars.......1 Chaos Cult

BILE'S ALLIANCE

THE SHRIVEN

Black Legionnaire Infantry...................5 Warbands
Vassal Renegades ....3 Warbands
Traitor Armour/Daemon Engines ......[Approx. 19 squadrons/packs]
Cults of Dessah .... 11 Chaos Cults

THE SPIDER'S CREATURES

Terata..Numbers variable
Surgeon Acolytes ....1 Coven

IMPERIAL TORCHBEARERS

THE AURIC CONQUERORS SHIELD HOST

The Solar Heralds .... 1 Shield Company
The Blades of Terra................... 1 Shield Company
The Brethren Adonite .... 1 Shield Company
The Emperor's Hands............... 1 Shield Company
Maximus Auxilia .... 18 Assets

CRIMSON SPIDERS CADRE

Prosecutors.....................................4 Squads
Vigilators...5 Squads
Witchseekers ....3 Squads
Supporting APCs................................12 Vehicles

EXECUTION FORCE REGNUM TRIBUNAL

Vindicare Assassin ....Codename 'Monarch'
Callidus Assassin ....Codename 'Majesty'
Eversor Assassin ....Codename 'Regent'
Culexus Assassin.......................Codename 'Jester'

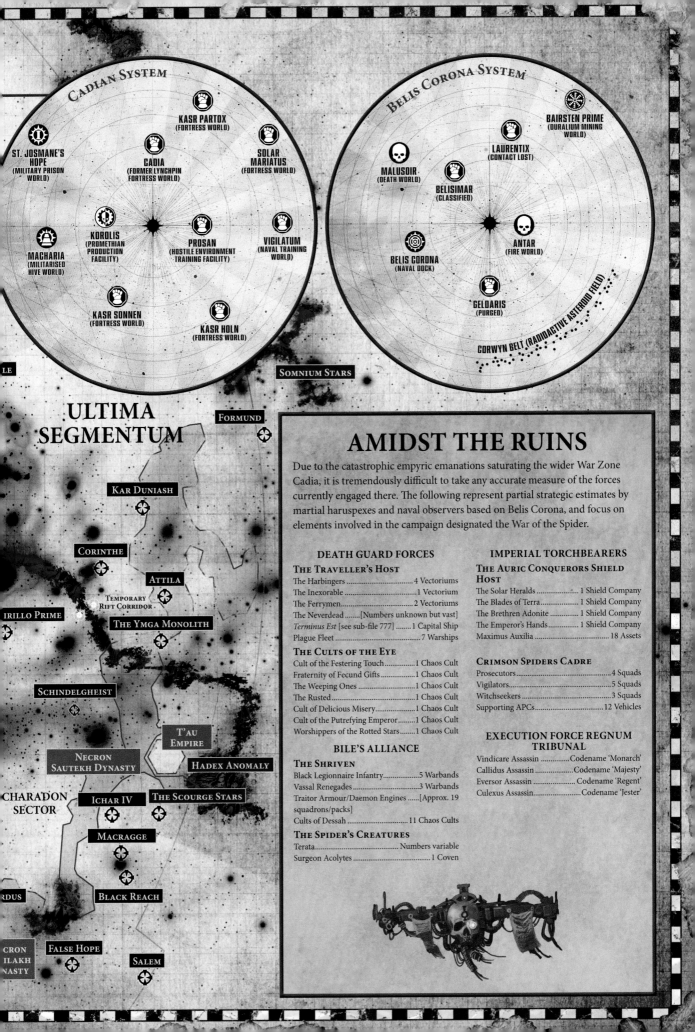

AMBUSH ON LIMAXIS

By the time Fabius Bile joined his forces to the Black Legionnaires of the Shriven, Typhus and his Plague Fleet were close on his heels. Recognising that swift action was crucial, Bile wasted no time convincing the Enlightener to mobilise his forces in exchange for certain 'gifts' of augmentation.

The poisonous light of a mutant star painted the brutish towers and redoubts of Dessah as Fabius Bile and Argento Corian cemented their alliance. Bile co-opted a sprawling suite of bio-warded vaults within which to continue his great works. He concealed the Ark Cornucontagious behind runic locks and servitor guns, then set his acolytes to work augmenting an initial wave of Shriven warriors. The Enlightener, it seemed, had lost none of the strategic cunning or charisma from his days as a loyalist Chapter Master. Bile saw evidence of not only a prodigious private army of Heretic Astartes serving at Corian's whim, but also hordes of cultists, mutants and rogue psykers as well as a menacing complement of traitor warships that prowled the void beyond Dessah's orbital envelope. Bile knew he could do much with such resources, but time was of the essence. Even as he worked upon Corian's bio-augmentations in person, the Spider urged his new employer to swift action against the approaching threats.

Though he was initially fixated upon his Imperial pursuers, the Enlightener soon grasped the true scale of the more immediate peril represented by Typhus' Death Guard. He might have been expected to fly into a rage when he realised the size of the army that pursued his new ally. He did not. The elixirs Bile had injected him with had made Corian stronger, but had also plunged the hooks of addiction and dependency into his soul. Coupled with certain subtle but invasive augmentations the Spider had wrought within his nervous system, the Enlightener was now Fabius Bile's creature whether he wished it or no.

Warp auguries by Corian's slave-sorcerers suggested that Typhus' flagship, the dreaded *Terminus Est*, was but days from exiting the warp above Dessah. Worse, the omens told of a fleet of plague ships sailing in his polluted wake, all of them packed to the gunwales with the diseased worshippers of Nurgle. If Typhus' force was allowed to attack the Shriven in such strength then the fight might well go ill for Bile and his new allies. Even if they prevailed against the Traveller,

---

The Enlightener thumped his fist against the runic access plate. He scowled as the armoured portal before him remained resolutely closed. Servitor guns in the corridor's ceiling swivelled, levelling their muzzles menacingly in his direction.

Corian stood back, his scowl deepening. The former Chapter Master was not used to doors within his own sanctum being locked against him. He found himself both angry and deeply disquieted. Corian was far from a fool; he knew that a deal with Fabius Bile was a dangerous bargain indeed. He also knew from experience that when one existed within the war-torn wilderness of the Cadian Gate, dangerous bargains were the only ones worth striking.

'Bile, a word if I might?' said Corian loudly into the corridor's still air. He knew the door had external vox pickups, and he was further certain that the Spider would have left them active. Surely even Fabius Bile was not so arrogant as to believe that he could burrow like a parasite into the Enlightener's fortress without being called upon to account for his actions.

Sure enough, the door hissed open. Sounds of whirring saw blades, splattering fluids and agonised screaming washed out along with a strange-smelling vapour. Amidst the clouds stood Bile. The armatures of his Chirurgeon clicked and twitched menacingly, yet upon his face the ghost of a mocking smile clung to the corners of his mouth.

'My lord Enlightener, how may I serve my valued ally and master?'

'When you requested medicae facilities to proceed with your work, I did not realise you would fortify them against me. What are you doing in there, Bile?'

Fabius' smile broadened, though the action did not reach his eyes.

'My lord, it is merely that the works in which I and my acolytes are engaged require a certain... stability and peace... to achieve their best results. But of course, my lord, you are welcome to step within my sanctum and see for yourself what transpires within your walls.'

Corian was wary, but he could hardly shy away from entering chambers within his own fortress. He gave a curt nod and stepped through the gloomy portal, not at all liking the smile that Bile offered him in return.

the Shriven would be decimated, left powerless to stop the Imperial forces also drawing closer by the day.

A pre-emptive strike was required, to bleed Typhus' forces so badly that their attack would stall, or be called off altogether. The Enlightener suggested the world of Limaxis. Though Dessah shared its local space with a handful of gas giants and radiation-bathed hellscapes, Limaxis was the only nominally habitable planet that now lay between Typhus and his quarry. In the wake of whatever catastrophe destroyed its cities, Limaxis' oceans had risen to swallow all but one of its landmasses. This region, now known only as the Drowning Wastes, had become a swampy morass from which rose the rusting cadavers of dead hive cities and long-abandoned Imperial fortifications. Such terrain was hardly the ideal theatre in which to face the relentless Death Guard or their corrupting plagues, but with their strategic options limited, Bile and Corian elected to proceed.

Moving fast, the Enlightener mobilised almost half of his military assets. He and Bile led a formidable force into the void towards Limaxis, accompanied by the first batch of grotesquely altered Shriven – known as the Terata – and augmented with certain arcane technologies that Bile had accumulated over his long years. Their plan was set. The Spider was determined to drive Typhus from his trail, and cared little for what this would cost his allies.

DANGEROUS PREY

Since departing the Scourge Stars upon Bile's trail, Typhus and his vectoriums had been guided by the otherworldly senses of caged daemonic predators. The vile liquid entities had followed the Spider's psychic spoor with much ill-natured hissing and bubbling, but when they suddenly went into a rabid frenzy

Typhus took note. Surely, suddenly, he was all but on top of his prey!

The *Terminus Est* tore its way through the ectoplasmic meniscus of realspace like a putrid maggot bursting from the flesh of a corpse. Wallowing plague ships followed it out, all of them quickly detecting the frantic distress calls echoing across long-range vox. It was the work of moments to confirm the choral signifier as belonging to the *Wretch*, the warship aboard which Bile had made good his escape some weeks earlier; the vessel hung in low orbit over a nearby world, its warp engines dead, its blast-riddled hull bleeding atmosphere. There were life signs aboard, but they were faint.

Suspecting a trap, Typhus elected not to board the crippled craft. Instead he commanded carefully targeted salvoes of lance fire that shot out the *Wretch*'s remaining engines and sent it shuddering down into the planet's atmosphere. Let the ship crash down upon that marshy world, Typhus thought. The Ark was an artefact blessed by Nurgle himself, and would come to no harm. As for Bile and whatever followers he had left, Typhus doubted they would prove as durable.

It seemed as though someone survived aboard the *Wretch*, however. The ship fired emergency atmospheric thrusters that turned its plunge into a graceless glide and saw it splash down a few miles south of a toppled hive spire. The impact was enough to tear the *Wretch* in two and leave its innards strewn across a dozen miles of swampland. Typhus did not care; he ordered his ships to settle in orbit, then led a substantial invasion force down to the surface to claim his prize and, ideally, Bile's rotting head.

Rust-pocked landers and attack craft rumbled down through Limaxis' atmosphere, foul pollutants and unholy plague spores trailing behind them. One by one the noxious vessels settled in the planet's shallow waters and spread slicks of foulness across the surface. Thrumming clouds of plague flies boiled from the landers' noisome interiors as Plague Marines, diseased cultists and bloated Daemon Engines disembarked in great number. Plagueburst Crawlers threw up great fans of putrid mud as their treads churned in the filth. Led by Typhus' trusted lieutenants, the warbands waded through the mire and took up positions upon islands of comparatively solid ground around the crash site. Typhus and his entourage of Blightlord Terminators entered the wreck, following flickering energy signatures to where they believed Bile must have concealed the Ark.

Typhus was more than displeased when, instead of his precious relic, he found himself confronted with a rabble of half-dead slave clones and an extremely large bomb. The explosion sent rolling waves through the swamp water and blazing wreckage crashing down amidst the alarmed Death Guard. Before its echoes had even died away the traitors' vox channels filled with gurgling cries of distress from on high. The plague ships were under attack!

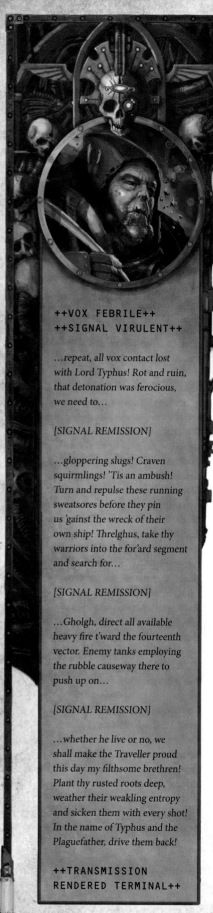

++VOX FEBRILE++
++SIGNAL VIRULENT++

...repeat, all vox contact lost with Lord Typhus! Rot and ruin, that detonation was ferocious, we need to...

[SIGNAL REMISSION]

...gloppering slugs! Craven squirmlings! 'Tis an ambush! Turn and repulse these running sweatsores before they pin us 'gainst the wreck of their own ship! Threlghus, take thy warriors into the for'ard segment and search for...

[SIGNAL REMISSION]

...Gholgh, direct all available heavy fire t'ward the fourteenth vector. Enemy tanks employing the rubble causeway there to push up on...

[SIGNAL REMISSION]

...whether he live or no, we shall make the Traveller proud this day my filthsome brethren! Plant thy rusted roots deep, weather their weakling entropy and sicken them with every shot! In the name of Typhus and the Plaguefather, drive them back!

++TRANSMISSION
RENDERED TERMINAL++

Slipping from behind the concealment of Bile's pilfered and retrofitted Commorrite night shields, four Shriven warships dove into the midst of Typhus' unsuspecting Plague Fleet. The dark of the void lit up with flickering lance fire and the rippling fire-blooms of broadside after broadside as the Black Legionnaires punished their diseased enemies for their incaution. The *Lamentation* was destroyed entirely, its blazing wreckage filling the Limaxian skies with streaks of fire as it broke up. The *Moribund*, the *Feculent Gift* and the *Rancid Blade* were all heavily damaged. Recognising that their position was untenable, the last three untouched plague ships broke orbit amidst flurries of diseased ordnance and drove for clear space in the hopes of re-forming and launching a determined counter-attack.

Dreadclaw Drop Pods and armoured gunships streaked down from the launch bays of the Shriven cruisers, bearing Bile, Corian and their followers to war. At the same time, advance bands of Terata – who had landed on the planet the day before and advanced under a blanket of sorcerous concealment – hurled themselves against the Death Guard defences. The thump of bolters and the boom of heavy artillery echoed across the foetid marshes as Typhus' forces let fly. Altered warriors dropped, thrashing and gushing boiling ichor as their wounded bodies self-destructed. Dreadclaws hit the mire amidst immense plumes of dirty water, disgorging squads of Black Legionnaires who hammered the Death Guard with close-ranged fire then charged their positions with chainswords howling. The Enlightener himself hovered from his transport's ramp surrounded by a furious psychic corona, drifting into the battle with beams of ravening warp energy leaping from his blazing eyes. Bile, meanwhile, shadowed his puppet warlord, his clipped orders sending in howling bands of altered warriors to drive back any Plague Marines who looked to be staging a breakout.

The Death Guard positions recoiled and contracted like wounded molluscs. Plague cultists died in droves, herded mercilessly onto the ambushers' guns in order to give their masters the chance to stage a fighting retreat. Using the wreck of the *Wretch* for cover, Typhus' warriors dug in and kept firing. Other forces might have panicked or been overrun as the Shriven pressed home their attack, but the Death Guard are known for their tenacity above all things, and they displayed it now.

Their faith was rewarded as a terrible droning buzz filled the air and, wreathed in the daemonic insect swarms of the Destroyer Hive, Typhus led his surviving Blightlords from the burning heart of the wreck. Scorched, wounded, but very much alive, the Traveller rallied an armoured fist of Daemon Engines about him before launching a spearhead assault that butchered more than two dozen Terata and stalled the Black Legion momentum.

As the enemy pounded his warriors with harassing fire and probed for weaknesses, Typhus used the powers of a slave-sorcerer to contact his plague ship captains in orbit. What he learned gave the Death Guard fresh heart; successfully reforming their line, the plague ships *Filthmonger*, *Vermian Curse* and *Leper's Blood* had driven the Shriven cruisers back, mauling both the *Hand of Darkness* and the *Bloodied Talon* in the process. Typhus' captains requested permission to press their attack and smash the smaller Shriven fleet, but the Traveller refused. Instead he had the least damaged of his ships form a blockade to hold the Shriven craft at bay. Meanwhile, the *Moribund* and the *Rancid Blade* settled low in Limaxis' atmosphere and unleashed carefully targeted creeping bombardments. As lance beams and plague bombs screamed down from on high, the outermost Shriven support elements suddenly found themselves in the midst of a devastating firestorm. Herded inwards by the encircling fire patterns, Bile and his forces found themselves caught between ruinous detonations to their rear and the thundering guns of the Death Guard to the fore.

Worse was to follow as fresh waves of Death Guard made planetfall amidst storms of fire to the north, south-east and south-west of the crash site. From their lowered ramps issued wave upon wave of plague-ridden Poxwalkers. The grinning, groaning zombies spilled from their landing craft like vomit and encircled the Black Legion with the horrible inevitability of a wasting sickness. It appeared that the ambushers were now caught in their own barbed web.

The Limaxis offensive had never been intended as a fight to the death, however, and Bile and Corian had their contingencies in place. Vox signals flashed northwards to where three of the Brazen Drakes' renegade Thunderhawks and an ancient Emperor's Children Stormbird waited amidst the shadows of a rusting Imperial hangar. Not for nothing had Bile conditioned his slave clones to bring the *Wretch* down where they had. Tangled screens of foliage burned away as the four heavy gunships burst from concealment with a scream of powerful engines. Blitzing the Death Guard's northernmost landing site as they went, the aircraft made for the looming hulk of a drowned hab-block that had been designated as the Black Legion extraction site.

Led by Corian and the last of Bile's first wave of Terata, the Spider's surviving forces cut a bloody path through the groaning Poxwalkers to reach the slumped hab-stack. Post-human warriors were dragged down and buried by mounds of grinning neverdead, their armour peeled off them bit by bit, their eye-lenses smashed out and questing fingers thrust into the gelid orbs beneath. Yet with Bile's augmented warriors rending, hacking and bludgeoning at the fore, and Corian's psychic blasts reducing swathes of Poxwalkers to ash, the Black Legion reached their objective. Bile himself led the push up the hab-stack's tilted, creeper-hung stairways and was the first to reach the lowered boarding ramp of his Stormbird.

Typhus halted amidst the turgid swamp waters and watched the enemy gunships streaking away into cloudy skies. Bitterness rose like vomit at the back of his throat.

Bile had escaped his vengeance.

The Ark was still lost. Worst of all, Typhus saw now the trap that the Spider had laid for him here. Looking around, he could not dispute that Bile and whatever fools now served him had done the Death Guard significant damage.

'Too impetuous, too eager to shame your gene-sire,' he muttered to himself. 'You should have seen that from leagues away you rot-begotten fool.'

Ignoring the quizzical looks of his Blightlord Terminators, Typhus beckoned to Fluxligh. The slave-sorcerer shambled forward, yellowed eyes glinting warily beneath his tattered cowl.

'I would speak with Plague Captain Sputimus,' growled Typhus. Fluxligh winced then nodded and began weaving his claw-like hands before his face. The slave-sorcerer muttered phlegm-thick incantations. Typhus' Destroyer Hive thrummed with agitation as the energies of the warp twisted and roiled. Then Fluxligh threw back his head with a pained groan, and the voice of Plague Captain Sputimus spilled from his mouth.

'Lord Typhus, I serve,' wheezed Sputimus from his throne aboard the *Filthmonger*.

'Plague Captain, our coward foes think to flee the battle aboard gunships. Target them from orbit and slay them all.'

'It cannot be done sire,' came Sputimus' hoarse reply. 'Another enemy vessel has joined the fight. Battle barge, but recently turned renegade. Where it came from lord I do not know, one moment it was not there and the next... It slew the *Moribund* outright and it is all we can do to hold off the combined enemy flotilla. Auspex suggests the battle barge is moving to make trans-atmospheric rendezvous with the gunships you spoke of.'

Typhus' anger bubbled in his breast. His Destroyer Hive buzzed furiously and for a moment he toyed with the idea of commanding his captains to press the attack.

'Pull back,' he said instead. 'Harass them, but let them depart. We must preserve what strength we have left if we are to prevail in our hunt.'

DEATH ON BAIRSTEN

With the immediate threat staved off, the Shriven found themselves with a window of time in which to gather their strength and plan their next moves. However, cracks were already appearing in the alliance between Bile and the Enlightener.

In the days following their triumphal return from Limaxis, the Shriven moved with even greater confidence. They had outmanoeuvred and – to their minds – outfought Typhus himself. Having seen how ferociously the Terata fought, they were able to gloss over the horrors of the warriors' demise, and Bile found himself with no shortage of willing test subjects for his surgeries. Warbands of Shriven took to the warp aboard swift frigates, returning with more luckless 'raw materials' for his elixirs and experiments. The Spider worked busily day and night.

But Argento Corian was less than delighted with Bile's successes. The Enlightener was sharply conscious that, day by day, his authority was being undermined. With Bile's compounds running through his veins, he could not bring himself to act against the parasite he had invited into his fortress. He could, however, remind his followers who their true master was. This he resolved to do.

Auguries and daemonic whispers revealed that the Imperial retribution force was now only a handful of short warp jumps away. Corian's seers told him that his enemies had halted in the Belis Corona System and were currently in orbit over the world of Bairsten Prime. Corian announced that he would not cower and wait for his enemies to beard him in his lair. Instead he mustered all but the most essential garrison forces and took ship at once for the Belis Corona System. Bile accompanied him at the head of his latest batch of altered warriors, yet he had little interest in supporting what he saw as the Enlightener's posturing. Instead, Bile had his own agenda upon Bairsten Prime…

ON HOSTILE CURRENTS

Shield-Captain Tyvar had led his Torchbearers through the war-torn Nachmund Gauntlet, through the fringes of War Zone Vigilus and on into the very rim of the Eye of Terror. He and his comrades had remained strong, their purpose unwavering, but their road had been perilous indeed. Even with a full Cadre of Silent Sisters scattered across their craft, each warp jump through the storms of the Imperium Nihilus had been hellish. They had faced hostile forces time and again. They had suffered losses. Now, with their quarry close at hand and the moment of truth almost upon them, Shield-Captain Tyvar had elected to re-arm and repair his surviving forces before running his prey to ground.

Tyvar's hopes of refitting at the naval docks of Belis Corona were dashed; that mighty fortress was beset by myriad foes, and what resources it had were required to keep its own fleets operational. Instead, Tyvar's task force settled into high orbit above Bairsten Prime in the hopes that the Tech-Magi who ran its famed duralium mines could be prevailed upon to effect repairs.

In fact, the Torchbearers found a world abandoned and fallen into ruin. What catastrophe had overtaken Bairsten Prime was unclear, but repeating warnings cycled across every vox frequency, beseeching all to avoid this cursed world in the Omnissiah's name. Tyvar was in no mood to heed such ghostly deterrents, however; not when auspex confirmed vast quantities of refined duralium languishing in rusted silos within a complex signified as Refinery XVI. Leaving his own Tech-Adepts to make what repairs they could upon his warships, the Shield-Captain led his forces to the surface. They dove through its furious electrical storms to claim the resources they required.

Such was the Imperial disposition when the Enlightener and his fleet tore their way from the warp into the Belis Corona System. Swift and powerful though they

'I feel it at work within me. I feel myself changing. Becoming stronger, faster, greater than ever before! I hunger for death… for slaughter… death! Slaughter! Strong! Nnnnyyeeaaagh!'

- Vox record of Subject 22/4 Delta, unintelligible beyond this point

were, the Imperial warships were in the midst of repairs. Heavy shuttles plied the void between the ships and the surface refinery. Presented with the sudden threat of an advancing Black Legion fleet, Shield-Captain Tyvar's ships could do little more than fend off the heretic ships with battery fire and do what they could to protect the vulnerable ore shuttles.

The Enlightener had little interest in the Imperial ships, however; his quarry lay on the planet below, for he had sworn before all his warriors that he would slay Atal Tyvar in single combat. The enemy's fleet could be dealt with later, once the warriors they transported had been slain. On Corian's orders, flights of armoured gunships and combat landers flurried from the embarkation decks of his cruisers. Escorted by flights of Black Legion Heldrakes, they swept down upon Bairsten's equatorial mining plains and the isolated life-signs around Refinery XVI.

The leading Shriven dropships were met by ferocious anti-aircraft fire. Tyvar had awoken the servitor crews of the refinery's Icarus turrets; now the weapons tracked and span, barrels thumping as they fired clouds of flak shells up at the descending craft. Heldrakes pinwheeled away trailing flames and wing fragments. A heavy lander detonated, raining wreckage and blazing bodies down upon the refinery. It was Bile who gave the order for the Shriven to redirect their assault, sending their dropships swooping away towards the small industrial spaceport a mile to the south.

Three such ports serviced the complex; solid, utilitarian assemblages of landing pads and outbuildings, all connected to the refinery by mag-rails set atop high rocky causeways. Shield-Captain Tyvar had set squads of Custodians to defend each of them. As the Shriven craft swept down one after another upon the southern port,

however, it rapidly became clear that the odds were impossible, even for warriors of the Adeptus Custodes. Shrugging off hammering volleys of fire from the dropships, the Custodians fell back with their guardian spears blazing, and fled along the causeway.

Corian and his Shriven were right on their heels. Bile, for his part, hung back, marshalling a sizeable force of Terata before following more cautiously in the Enlightener's wake. His approach proved prudent as, halfway along the causeway, a band of Vertus Praetors struck. They had streaked in low, using the rocky bulk of the causeway to mask their approach. Now they reared suddenly into view amidst the howl of powerful engines and subjected the Shriven to a punishing salvo of missiles. As they did, the retreating Custodes turned and let fly. Explosions tore Heretic Astartes apart. A Shriven Predator detonated with a fiery roar, chunks of its wreckage spinning away ablaze.

The Enlightener's furious oaths echoed across the lightning-lashed plains. The air quivered with empyric tension before the altered sorcerer unleashed a furious storm of psychic energies into the causeway. Even the vaunted aegis of the Emperor was not enough to stop this explosion of raw force, which hurled three of the Custodians from the causeway and sent two Dawneagle jetbikes spinning away to explode on the hard bedrock below.

Again the surviving Imperial forces fell back and again the Shriven gave chase. Again Bile hung back amidst the bulk of the assault force,

watching with detached interest as Corian and his Chosen warriors reached the railhead in the shadow of the refinery's towers. Here the Imperial forces struck again, bolters and flamers roaring as squads of Null-Maidens sprung an ambush of their own. Even Bile recoiled at the null-aura that the Silent Sisters projected, while Corian – front and centre in the renegade battle line – howled in agony at the sudden stifling of his empyric senses.

The attack might have faltered there and then, but Bile hissed orders of his own. Altered warriors and flesh-twisted Bikers bulled their way to the fore with Bile in their

midst and hurled themselves at the outnumbered foe. At the same time the surviving Heldrakes swept back in, their draconic shadows criss-crossing the engagement area as warpflames belched from their maws.

Once more the Imperial forces fell back in good order, leaving their fallen blazing or bolt-riddled in their wake. This time the Enlightener halted; he had successfully claimed a beachhead upon the rocky plateau that housed the refinery proper, but only thanks to Bile's quick thinking. Conscious that his control was slipping, and perhaps his sanity with it, the Enlightener fought to think clearly and strategise. Snapping out orders, he broke his surviving warriors into several smaller warbands, each supported by Obliterators and Daemon Engines, each led in by squads in Rhino APCs who could watch for further traps as the Shriven pushed forward. Auspex showed the majority of the foe gathered around the macro-silos at the refinery's heart, and so the Shriven pushed that way through the tangle of rusted machinery, creaking cranes and abandoned structures.

Bile, however, split his small force off from the main advance. Corian was only too happy to see him go, ordering only that Bile should stay out of his way. The Spider, for his part, was also pleased, for here was a rare chance to harvest fine specimens for his great work. He vanished into the gloomy alleys between the refinery's towering buildings, taking with him several squads of his most heavily altered followers as well as a gaggle of gibbering acolytes clad in rubberised surgical gear.

Again the Imperial forces struck at the Shriven, and again. Now, though, the Heretic Astartes met them with disciplined fire and vicious counter-assaults that saw even the Adeptus Custodes driven back. At last Corian led the way into the refinery's central processing yard amidst blizzards of psychic fire. There the Shriven met the main strength of the Imperial force and, had their master been in his right mind, they might have rethought their assault. Shield-Captain Tyvar had gathered a formidable force of Custodians and Null-Maidens around him, Venerable Contemptor Dreadnoughts and even Land Raiders rumbling up in support. Yet Bile's twisted surgery had done terrible things to the Enlightener, and to many of his followers. Unable to restrain their psychotic battle-lust, they hurled themselves into a maniacal charge and battle was joined. As the fighting raged, none noticed the dark figure that crouched amidst the rusting walkways of a macro-silo high above. The figure stayed still as death, a long and deadly-looking rifle cradled in its hands.

Bile heard it all from a distance, the muffled thunder of gunfire and the clash of blades echoing to where he and his warriors stalked in the shadows. They had circumnavigated the refinery until they reached a separate causeway that connected to another of the complex's spaceports. As Bile had hoped, a single Custodian Warden and an under-strength squad of Null-Maidens lingered here. They were clearly dying to join the battle, but duty compelled them to watch over the continued efforts of heavy servitors still ferrying shipments of duralium into waiting mag-carriages and thence to the shuttles docked at the spaceport below.

Only too glad to offer his enemies a taste of the fighting they had been denied, Bile loosed his Terata on them. Altered warriors surged forward with lunatic howls, shrugging off direct hits from bolt rounds and the slashing kiss of powered blades. Deformed limbs and heads span away as the Imperial warriors hacked and

hewed furiously. Yet Bile's warriors were relentless; they felt neither pain nor fear, bloodshot eyes bulging and foul appendages thrashing as they surrounded their victims and sought not to kill them, but to wound, weaken and finally grapple them to the ground. As the fight turned his way, Bile strode forward, the Rod of Torment tapping with every pace. With surgical precision the Spider shot each of his victims in turn, aiming for exposed armour joints and bared flesh. His Xyclos Needler hissed like a serpent as it spat one dart after another, each loaded with tremendously powerful paralysing toxins of Bile's own manufacture. As each victim fell, Bile's twisted acolytes descended on them and dragged them away into the shadows.

Only now that he had his harvest did the Spider turn and lead the last of his altered warriors back to Corian's aid. He arrived in time to see the Shriven hard-pressed and teetering upon the brink of collapse. The Enlightener himself, however, was hanging suspended in a corona of witchfire, eyes blazing and hands outstretched as he drove Shield-Captain Tyvar to his knees. It was then that the echoing crack of a high-powered sniper rifle cut through the din of battle. Corian jerked in mid-air. Blood puffed from the side of his skull. His fires blinked out in a heartbeat and his body crashed heavily to the ground.

The battle ended in that moment. In the rout that followed, only the martial might of the Shriven allowed them to execute a fighting retreat to their drop craft. Amidst the mayhem and bloodshed, Bile's Terata bore the twitching body of Argento Corian from the field. Bile led them, gunning down the few loyalists who barred his path and smiling all the while.

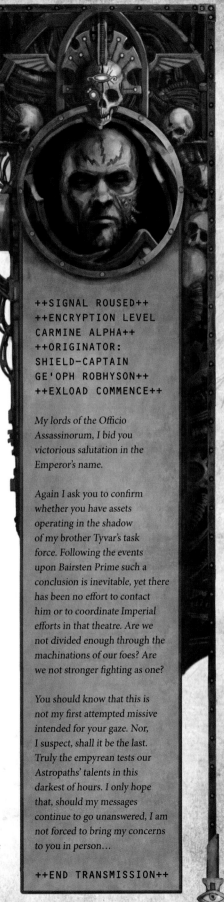

++SIGNAL ROUSED++
++ENCRYPTION LEVEL CARMINE ALPHA++
++ORIGINATOR: SHIELD-CAPTAIN GE'OPH ROBHYSON++
++EXLOAD COMMENCE++

My lords of the Officio Assassinorum, I bid you victorious salutation in the Emperor's name.

Again I ask you to confirm whether you have assets operating in the shadow of my brother Tyvar's task force. Following the events upon Bairsten Prime such a conclusion is inevitable, yet there has been no effort to contact him or to coordinate Imperial efforts in that theatre. Are we not divided enough through the machinations of our foes? Are we not stronger fighting as one?

You should know that this is not my first attempted missive intended for your gaze. Nor, I suspect, shall it be the last. Truly the empyrean tests our Astropaths' talents in this darkest of hours. I only hope that, should my messages continue to go unanswered, I am not forced to bring my concerns to you in person…

++END TRANSMISSION++

THE UNRAVELLING WEB

Bile and the surviving Shriven retreated to Dessah, falling back behind their fortress' high battlements and gun emplacements. With the Enlightener apparently slain, his former followers looked to Bile for leadership. They were his creatures now, just as he had planned all along. Yet peril drew closer by the day.

The Shriven seers wailed of not one but two foes drawing closer with every passing hour. In desperation, some amongst the warband beseeched Fabius Bile to aid them, while others muttered darkly that the Spider had already done more than enough. For his part, Bile was satisfied with events. He had not predicted Corian's fall upon Bairsten and had some grave suspicions about its authors, but he had been quick to capitalise upon this unexpected boon. Bile had made great strides behind the sealed doors of his laboratory. Now he sought to make good his escape.

Bile gathered the Shriven within the Enlightener's grand throne room and addressed them. He spoke of his desire to see these invaders crushed, both the filth-ridden Death Guard and the presumptuous corpse-worshippers. He could do it, he said, but not without the complete loyalty of the remaining Shriven. This was at last too much for Argento Corian's surviving Chosen. Tempers flared as they accused the rest of their warband of being duped. They called Bile an opportunist ghoul, cursed the day he had come to Dessah, and laid the Enlightener's death firmly at Bile's feet. At this, the Spider merely smiled and signalled his surgeon-acolytes to unveil his latest masterpiece.

Argento Corian was much changed. The parts of his brain not destroyed by the round passing through his skull had been scooped out by Bile's Chirurgeon. The altered golem that stalked into the throne room was the Enlightener in name only. Bulging red eyes stared from a face riven with stitch marks, scarified runes and wires. His armour strained to contain his muscle-bulked physique. Pipes and tubes gurgled with weird fluids, flushing them through Corian's armour and body alike. Unbridled psychic potential crackled around the Enlightener, though with his skull emptied of its contents all but Fabius Bile wondered how such a thing could be.

Incensed, those loyal to Corian's former incarnation went for their blades. The Enlightener annihilated them with beams of psychic fire. Bile asked again for the loyalty of the Shriven, and this time, standing over the blackened and mangled remains of their former comrades, they agreed to a man.

Bile planned to augment every remaining Shriven Chaos Space Marine. He ordered all defenders concentrated within Dessah's Primary Bastion, which was partially built into a towering mountain. He commanded that the outer defences be demolished and laced with booby traps, ensuring his enemies would have to come at him through a lethal killing zone. When the foe attacked, the Enlightener and the Shriven were to stand firm in the fortress' defence, drawing the foe in and pinning them before the walls. Only then would Bile unleash his master stroke. A flight of modified Heldrakes would belch neurotoxin fumes over the battle. Bile assured his followers this would

---

High above Dessah, a sleek black warship slid from the warp like a dagger drawn from its sheath. Within its shadowy corridors, stern-faced adepts in black bodygloves worked efficiently beneath the glow of crimson lumens. Elsewhere aboard the craft, four supremely dangerous individuals readied themselves for action: one sat in meditation, rifle across his knees; one lurked in a darkened cell with his cursed eye shut tight; one endured agonising anatomical shifts and shudders as she adopted her polymorphine-enhanced disguise; and one twitched and grunted within a webwork of cables, his murderous body chemically restrained while strategic inloads flowed into his subconscious mind.

On the bridge, arcane psi-spoor auspexes chimed softly as they confirmed that the target was on the world below and that – in some form or other – he still lived.

The adepts reacted with continued calm. They thumbed runic controls, muttering the approved prayers as they activated the Execution Force assets one after another. A plan had already been decided upon by the craft's shadowy masters. The failed kill on Bairsten Prime might well have alerted both heretic and Imperial parties to the assassins' presence. Subtlety was a luxury they could no longer afford. Only the mission mattered at this juncture, and if it cost lives then so be it.

One by one the assets' small insertion craft streaked away into the atmosphere, down towards the battle raging on Dessah's surface.

leave them untouched while driving the Death Guard and Imperial warriors into a murderous frenzy. With their enemies lost to madness and tearing one another apart, Bile and the remaining Shriven could flee aboard a swift frigate and slip away into the warp.

Frenzied preparations followed Bile's pronouncements, and the Primary Bastion was ready by the time Typhus' plague ships appeared above Dessah. The Traveller had not been idle. Piratical raids of neighbouring systems had yielded the resources to repair his vessels. He had gathered cultists from seven different worlds, and swollen his depleted ranks further by the addition of thousands upon thousands of Poxwalkers. Now he was coming for the Ark Cornucontagious, and for revenge.

The surviving Shriven warships attempted to use Bile's night shields to ambush the Death Guard again. This time Typhus was ready. He had spread tracker entities across his fleet and given each of them the warp-scent of the Shriven. Thus, even as the Black Legion cruisers pounced, they found gun batteries primed and pointed right at them. Explosive carnage filled Dessah's orbital envelope. Wreckage rained down as flaming meteors through the planet's atmosphere. When the battle barge *Drake Rampant* attempted a desperate and horribly misjudged boarding assault against the *Terminus Est*, the battle swung in Typhus' favour. Soon enough the rusting, plague-riddled hulk of the *Drake Rampant* was tumbling away while Death Guard landers swept down upon the Primary Bastion.

Death Guard forces landed in great number amidst the fortress' outer defences. Booby traps detonated as shambling swarms of Poxwalkers triggered them. So numerous were the neverdead that the fiery blasts made barely a dent. Behind them came bands of Plague Marines escorting batteries of Plagueburst

Crawlers. The daemonic artillery spoke again and again, lofting hails of blight-laden shells through the air to slam against the fortress' walls. Soon enough they had blasted a wide and rotting breach.

Trudging masses of infantry made for the yawning rent in the fortress' walls, but here the Enlightener and his Shriven counter-attacked furiously. Blasts of psychic force ploughed through the Poxwalkers and hurled their broken corpses left and right. Altered warriors tore their shambling foes apart, slaughtering swathes of them for every Terata that was dragged down and torn to bits.

Yet all this was but a distraction. Even as the fighting raged down below, unclean energies flashed and crackled within the fortress. Typhus and his Terminator retinue stepped

from them with grim resolve; they had come for the Ark, and for Bile's head, and the sorcerous auspexes within their corrupt helms told them that both were nearby.

Bile was alerted to his peril by the thunder of servitor guns and the howling of daemonic guard-entities. He had laboured at his great works up to the last moment, but now he was concerned that his obsessive desire to keep experimenting might have led him to linger too long. Surgeon-acolytes began stowing his samples and wheeling bio-sarcophagi into anti-grav transit racks, but Bile knew that if Typhus was not slowed then they would never escape. Regretfully, the Spider activated his latest batch of altered warriors, the very finest of his creations from Dessah. Raving and frothing, the twisted monsters burst from the lab and surged into battle.

It was now, as the battle raged, that Tyvar and his Torchbearers arrived over Dessah. Acting swiftly, the Shield-Captain gathered what auspex and pict-data he could, formulated a robust plan, then led his forces down through the planet's atmosphere aboard armoured gunships. The craft streaked in low, hugging Dessah's rocky terrain to avoid detection. As the furious battle spread out before them, the bulk of the Imperial forces peeled off and made for the Death Guard's rear lines. The gilded gunships delivered Adeptus Custodes and Silent Sisters into the ruins, where they struck at the Daemon Engines still pummelling the fortress. Fighting raged through the ruins as Custodians hacked apart Myphitic Blight-Haulers, salvoes of blight shells laid gleaming Imperial heroes low, and one by one the Plagueburst Crawlers were blasted to scrap.

With the enemy guns silenced, the Adeptus Custodes and Null-Maidens turned for the breach. Their orders were to hack a path through the besieging hordes to where the Enlightener still fought and – now that the threat of plague bombardment had been removed – engage the turncoat sorcerer.

Meanwhile, a pair of Imperial gunships drew level with one of the Primary Bastion's upper casemates. They blasted a ragged hole in the structure then lowered their ramps and disgorged Shield-Captain Tyvar and two full squads of Allarus Custodians into the fortress' halls. Tyvar's warriors had made positive identification of Fabius Bile during the fighting on Bairsten Prime and Tyvar knew he had to try to slay the loathed heretic. Moreover, several of Tyvar's warriors had gone missing during that fight and he had little doubt that Bile was to blame. As he led his warriors through the fortress' corridors towards the sounds of battle, the Shield-Captain hoped he could rescue those comrades from Bile's twisted ministrations.

Minutes later Fabius Bile emerged from his laboratory and straight into the midst of a gun battle. Typhus and his surviving Terminators were trading furious volleys of fire with the advancing Shield-Captain and his Allarus Custodians, their conflict blocking Bile's route to freedom. With a snarl the Primogenitor launched himself into the fight even as Typhus bellowed in recognition. Bile raised his Xyclos Needler, raining toxic rounds upon his enemies and sending a Blightlord Terminator crashing to the ground. Several of Bile's surgeon-acolytes were gunned

down as they frantically shoved their armoured grav-reliquaries through the vicious crossfire, and even Bile himself grunted with pain as he was shot several times, his Chirurgeon clicking madly as it sought to seal his wounds.

Seeing his quarry about to escape, Typhus launched a headlong charge with his Manreaper swinging. Before the weapon could connect, Bile and the last of his underlings vanished through another armoured bulkhead that sealed behind them with a hiss and a clang. The next moment, Typhus found himself faced by the vengeful Shield-Captain and his Allarus Custodians. A glance at the ragged remains of his retinue told Typhus this was a fight he could not win. Spitting a vow to have his vengeance upon Bile, he chanted an incantation and was wreathed in a roaring storm of plague flies. When they dissipated the Traveller was gone, leaving the last of his warriors to face the fury of Tyvar and his companions alone.

At the breach, the Enlightener and his berserk warriors had torn and blasted so many foes that mountains of dead lay all around them. Yet their numbers too were dwindling. It was now that the Execution Force struck. First came

As one, the Heldrakes swept from their perches atop the mountain's peak. They screamed down upon the warriors battling furiously in the breach. The Enlightener was hammering the enemy hordes with one psychic blast after another, his Shriven laying down fusillades of fire as the last of their tanks fired again and again.

Still the Death Guard pressed forward, Poxwalkers in their hundreds clambering over their own fallen to totter into the fight. The neverdead buried the altered warriors with their numbers while Plague Marines raked the Black Legion lines with fire.

Further back, out amongst the ruins, the Imperial forces were cutting a gory swathe towards the breach, but their momentum was slowing in

the face of the relentless servants of Nurgle.

Now it was time to trigger yet more anarchy and bloodshed. One at a time the Heldrakes opened their jaws wide and, as they swooped low over the battle, breathed roiling clouds of mauve gasses across the combatants. Bile had possessed neither time nor inclination to tailor his toxins to his foes, but he had ample data concerning the altered biochemistry of his augmented Shriven. Thus, as the clouds drifted down and flowed into rebreathers and open mouths, it was the Enlightener and his warriors who were driven to new heights of berserk fury, not their foes. One last betrayal of his ill-fated allies by Fabius Bile; one last trick to ensure that they kept his pursuers busy long enough to cover his escape.

a rifle round, fired from atop a ruined spire. The Enlightener's head snapped up and he obliterated the bullet in mid-air with a psychic blast. The empyric bolt roared on, back up the shot's trajectory to impact with killing force. Amidst the explosion a ruined, black-clad figure tumbled blazing to its death.

Next came the Callidus, morphing into her true form as she suddenly emerged from amidst the Enlightener's shocked cultists. Her neural shredder howled as she blasted first one Shriven Terata, then another and another. Flipping over a fourth, the Callidus swept her phase sword around to decapitate the altered warrior, then drove the blade into the Enlightener's chest. The sorcerer roared with pain then blasted the lithe assassin backwards into a mound of corpses with another psychic pulse. Yet his bellow of triumph became a howl of agony as a beam of raw darkness hit him, banishing his psychic powers in an instant. The Enlightener looked up to see the eerie figure of a Culexus Assassin flickering towards him. Before the sorcerer could regather his powers the skull-masked figure of an Eversor Assassin tore through a knot of Terata like an artillery shell and ploughed into him. The frenzied assassin tore madly at the Enlightener. One hand was blown off by a bolt round from the Eversor's executioner pistol before the assassin's hypodermic talons sunk deep into the Enlightener's face. One eye punctured, flesh blackening with toxins, the altered sorcerer grabbed his assailant by the throat, lifted him high and snapped the assassin's neck with raw psychokinetic force.

The Enlightener enjoyed a moment of triumph before the Eversor's blood chemistry went into critical meltdown and his body exploded with the force of a demolition charge. As the dust settled, the ruptured corpse of the Enlightener finally twitched its last.

Their mission completed, the Culexus and wounded Callidus vanished into the anarchy of the battle. Yet in truth the conflict was done. A few tattered handfuls of Shriven remained, leaderless, lost to madness or fleeing wildly. As a warband they were utterly spent. Word had reached the Death Guard, meanwhile, that their master had returned to the Plague Fleet and had ordered them to fall back. Their quarry had escaped again. Full of bitterness and disgust, the Plague Marines quit the field.

Less than a quarter of Shield-Captain Tyvar's original forces remained to link up deep within the fortress and purge the revolting horrors remaining within Bile's abandoned laboratory. With their targets slain but their comrades lost to Bile's clutches, Tyvar believed it essential that word of what they had witnessed should find its way back to the Imperial authorities. This would be his new duty. Thus the Imperial warriors collected their fallen, lamented their lost, and left the Cadian Gate behind them.

As for Fabius Bile, he was not seen again upon Dessah – his ship had slipped away, a light frigate ghosting through the orbital debris fields and the last flickering exchanges of the void war before punching into warp space and making good its escape. The Primogenitor had work to do upon Urum, and he did not mean for it to be delayed…

Echoes of Awakening

All across the galaxy, voices are raised in terror, confusion, bloodlust and dark praise as the Great Rift yawns wide. Even within the beleaguered bounds of the Imperium Sanctus this cacophony of horrors is enough to drown the minds of the Astropaths forced to decipher them. Deep within the swirling madness of the Imperium Nihilus, meanwhile, those screams ring louder still.

+++

[Vox-Intercept: Cruor, Sub-sector Straziar]

'KILL! MAIM! BURN! KILL! MAIM! BURN! KILL! MAIM! BURN! KILL! MAIM! BURN! KILL! MAIM! BURN! KILL! MAIM! BURN! KILL! MAIM! BURN! KILL! MAIM! BURN! KILL! MAIM! BURN! KILL! MAIM! BURN! KILL! MAIM! BURN! KILL! MAIM! BURN! KILL! MAIM! BURN! KILL! MAIM! BURN! KILL! MAIM! BURN! KILL! MAIM! BURN!!'

Addendum: Vox transmission persists into its seventh solar month. QR, SM, PN, UF-3 through 8, KL, VT-x and VT-t all dispatched to location, all now declared lost. Feelings of despair and dread increasing. Dire omens reported by Conclave Liminas. I do not know why, but I fear what shall transpire if the recitation is not halted before it reaches its eighth solar month...

+++

Priority Missive //884IN
Category: Encounter — Hereticus
Diabolus Extremis
Clearance: Vermillion

Captain-General, glory of Terra to you my lord. Great have our travails been since departing the light of the Sol System, and dark our road. Even now I and my comrades hasten homeward, for we have borne witness to an evil that I believe constitutes a threat to our Master's realm. Should the storms close in upon us before we see Terra's light again, I hope that at the least this missive shall reach you that you might act in our stead. For the abominations you shall witness in the attached datascriptures I make no apology; it is crucial that you see as I have the extent of the horrors wrought by the heretic Fabius Bile. You must understand as I now do the true depths of evil with which we are faced.

Your servant and brother, Shield-Captain Atal Tyvar

+++

One by one we awaken them, channelling the energies of the unbridled cosmos through their void-cold cores. Around their feet we array our machines. In their hard black shadows our servants toil. Now comes silence, and stillness, and the abiding order of the empty aeons.

+++

+++Astropathic Communiqué+++
+++Duct Theta-Hespus-4+++
+++Origin: Crescent VI, Attillan Sub-Sector+++

This is Canoness Rosemaera Grace of the Order of the Argent Shroud calling any loyal Imperial forces. Let it be known that our vigil continues. We keep the faith upon Crescent VI though the storms empyric may surround us and the spirits of the damned may assail us. If you receive this message, know that our pyres work night and day to purge all those unclean from amongst our flock, but know also that their numbers grow daily while our own now dwindle. If you hear this and can come to our aid, then come armed with a hard heart and a blazing faith lest you too be found wanting. And if none are left to hear this... well then, Emperor, you have seen our works and our hearts, and you already know that we remained faithful to the end.

+++

>> Kardophor Prime / Hive Secundus
>> Precinct Prime Arbitratorial Rept
>> File 88-8-66-3-565-D

Heavy transport tug Slavish Devotion held at grav-anchor and boarded today at fifth bell. Initial search escalated to search and slay after limited exchange of firearms and empyric manifestation. Ten Arbitrators dead or wounded. Thirty-two heretic casualties. Six minor witches amongst their number. Note also that all heretics exhibited missing right eye. Wounds appear self-inflicted. This is the third such instance in this rotation. What in the Emperor's name is going on?

+++

He pilfers the secrets of his betters and calls himself wise, this grubbing mon-keigh physicker. He puts needle to flesh, threads his stitches and concocts his elixirs, yet against our puissant arts his efforts are as crude as a savage fashioning idols from ordure and mud. They call him Spider, Primogenitor, Clone Lord... laughable... to the Covens he is nought but prey, and now it is time to hunt.

+++

```
[Strategic Assessment K-F-554]
[Magos Metasuppositor Xyko Vengh]

Ork presence within quadrant
Aleph-7 through quadrant Aleph-13
has now increased by a factor
of 6.34. Empyric anomalies
manifesting along system-
parallel 0.045-0.121 have not
impacted xenos concentrations as
projected, but instead appear
to have increased projected
aggression response by a factor
of 3.4. Chances of victory
on Ryza now stand at 18 per
cent without introduction of
positive variables. Requests for
reinforcement pending...pending...
pending...
```

+++

I see a world of iron and of fire, studded with a million staring eyes. I see a blazing beacon, its radiance a flickering halo that cuts sharp as knives. I see a thousand, thousand shining darts that vanish into a howling void, each dwindling to the faintest speck before they are lost to me forever. I see a mountain crowned with thunderbolts whose roots shudder, and shatter, and crack. I see an end to all things and I hope that I am wrong. Yet hope has never been my friend or ally...

+++

```
[Vox-record commences]
Watch-Captain Hathchor reporting.
After severe disruption to our
voyage in the immaterium, we
finally translated into the Vaspa
System and established we had lost
forty-six days sidereal in the
warp. Of the T'au threat described
in the astropathic distress call
we found no sign, yet this world
is damned all the same. Rather
than a people conquered by xenos
we found a world of witches, whose
powers saw the aliens slain but
must surely also damn them to
their own certain destruction.
```

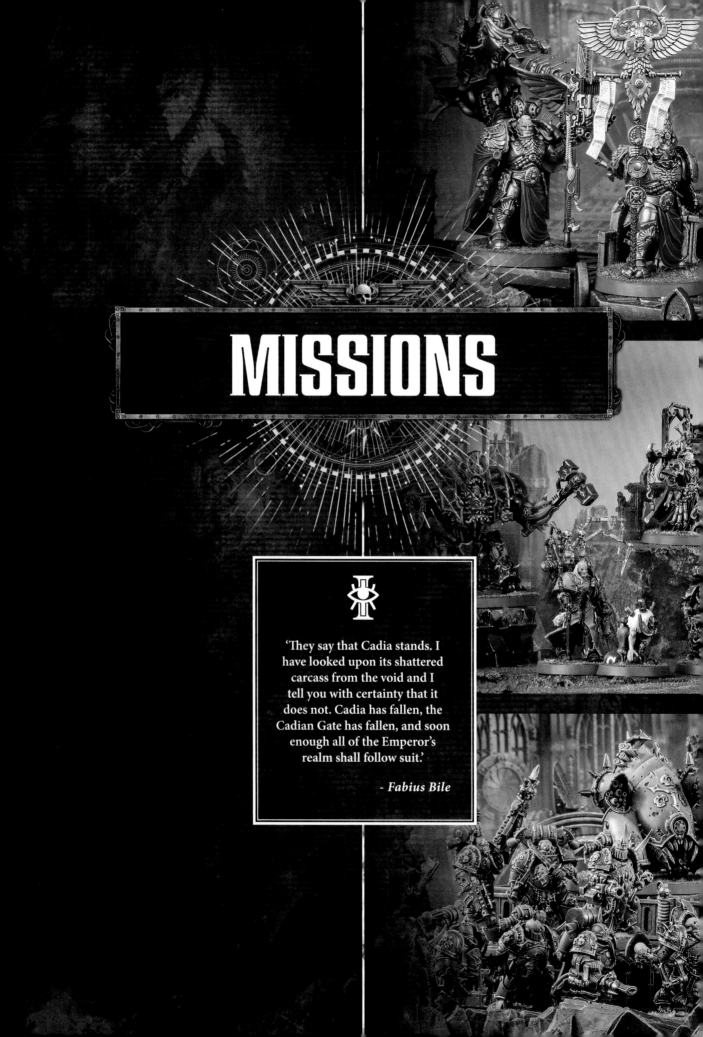

MISSIONS

'They say that Cadia stands. I have looked upon its shattered carcass from the void and I tell you with certainty that it does not. Cadia has fallen, the Cadian Gate has fallen, and soon enough all of the Emperor's realm shall follow suit.'

- *Fabius Bile*

THE THRESHING FIELDS

The rules presented in this section allow you to play games set in locations inspired by those found in the narrative of this book, as well as play through some of the most dramatic moments from the battles on Limaxis, Bairsten and Dessah. Will you command the elite Imperial forces, the putrid ranks of the Death Guard, or the abominable creations of Fabius Bile himself?

INTRODUCTION

This section starts by providing a new Theatre of War, designed to represent the battlefields of the War of the Spider. Agents of the Officio Assassinorum lurk in the shadows, waiting for the moment to strike their designated target, and will silence anyone who tries to interfere with their directives.

While these rules are designed for recreating the War of the Spider, they can be used and modified to represent any location where the Officio Assassinorum has an active interest. This could be a war zone in which enemies of the Imperium are arrayed on both sides of the conflict, or one in which loyal servants of the Emperor learn at gunpoint that they have

made enemies amongst the High Lords of Terra.

On pages 26-31, three new Crucible of War missions are presented for narrative play. Merciless Ambush allows players to fight out the harrowing battle on Limaxis, Hostile Acquisitions pits players against one another in a conflict such as that which took place on the mining plains of Bairsten, while Unexpected Quarters is based on the brutal events on Dessah.

THEATRES OF WAR

As the Enlightener and his warband of corrupted Space Marines join forces with Fabius Bile, they draw the ire of both the Imperium and the Death Guard. Though the Spider remains always one step ahead of his pursuers, the agents of the Officio Assassinorum have numerous ways of reaching their quarry.

In this section you will find an exciting new Theatre of War to use in your games of Warhammer 40,000. Theatres of War offer new tactical challenges to enrich your games, and introduce new rules to represent many varied battle environments. Some modify the core rules (e.g. by altering the range of weapons). Some provide new rules for phenomena like dust storms, volcanic eruptions and earthquakes. Some grant additional abilities and Stratagems to certain units.

These rules are designed to reflect the dangers faced by agents of the Officio Assassinorum on the battlefield, but they are entirely optional and, so long as you and your opponent agree, can be used in any Warhammer 40,000 game.

Agree which, if any, Theatre of War rules will be used when you are setting up the battlefield, before deployment.

THEATRE OF WAR: HOSTILE OPERATIVES

Assassins have taken up positions around the battlefield. They lie in wait, their amplified senses honed on their targets, and will reveal themselves only when the success of their mission is placed in jeopardy.

Before the battle, the players must gather at least one **Officio Assassinorum** unit. We recommend using between two and six **Officio Assassinorum** units to ensure this environment is suitably challenging. These are referred to as Assassin units.

Lurking in the Shadows: Before either side deploys, you must first infiltrate the battlefield with lurking Assassins. To do so, you will need six objective markers: if there are fewer than six objective markers on the battlefield, after setting up any mandatory objective markers required for the mission, set up additional objective markers until there are six (these additional objective markers must be set up more than 9" away from any other objective markers and not within 6" of any battlefield edge. They have no effect on any victory conditions). The players then randomly select, one at a time, a number of different objective markers equal to the number of Assassin units, setting up a randomly selected Assassin unit within 6" of each of those objective markers. Once all of the Assassin units have been set up, remove any additional objective markers that were set up.

Assassin Units: Assassin units are treated as enemy units by both players, and Assassin units treat each unit in a player's army as an enemy unit. Assassin units treat other Assassin units as friendly units. In the Fight phase, Assassin units fight after all other units unless they have charged in their turn (see below). If possible, in the Fight phase, each Assassin model will target the closest enemy **Character** unit with all of its attacks. If two units are equally close, randomly select which they will target with their attacks. When resolving attacks or making saving throws etc. for Assassin units, we recommend your opponent rolls the dice. The Command Re-roll Stratagem cannot be used to re-roll dice rolls made for Assassin units.

The Assassin Turn: At the end of each battle round, the Assassin units have a 'turn'. In their Movement phase, each Assassin unit will move as far as possible towards the closest enemy **Character unit** (unless they are already within 1" of one), but they will not Fall Back or Advance. In their Shooting phase, each model will shoot at the closest visible enemy **Character** unit within range, ignoring the usual restriction on targeting **Characters**. In their Charge phase, if two units are equally close, randomly determine which they will charge. In addition, if they are within 12" of any enemy **Character** units in their Charge phase, they will attempt to charge the closest enemy **Character** unit. In their Fight phase, Assassin units behave as described

previously. If any sequencing issues arise, the players roll off and the winner decides the order in which the rules in question are resolved.

The following additional rules apply to each type of Assassin:

CALLIDUS

- This model's Polymorphine ability is not used.
- Treat both players as being affected by this model's Reign of Confusion ability.
- At the start of its Movement phase, if this model is within 1" of an enemy unit that is not a **Character**, it will Fall Back. It must end this Fall Back as close as possible to the closest enemy **Character** unit.

CULEXUS

- If possible, then, instead of the closest **Character** unit, this model will always move towards the closest **Psyker** unit.
- If a **Psyker** is in range and visible to them, if able, this model will always target this unit instead of the closest **Character** unit.
- In its Charge phase, if there is a **Psyker** within 12" of this model, this model will always attempt to charge that model instead of the closest **Character** unit.
- In the Fight phase, this model will target a **Psyker** unit with attacks made with melee weapons.

EVERSOR

If no **Character** units are within range or visible to this model in the Assassin's Shooting phase, and the closest enemy unit is a **Vehicle**, if possible this model will attack with melta bombs instead of its executioner pistol.

VINDICARE

This model will never move in its Movement phase, unless it is within 1" of an enemy unit that is not a **Character**, in which case it will Fall Back. When it does so, it will move as fast as possible in order to end that move as far away as possible from any enemy models.

CRUCIBLE OF WAR
MERCILESS AMBUSH

The attacking force has lured their prey into a trap, and now look to press their advantage with a merciless assault. The defenders must regroup and hold firm, their resolve the only route to victory.

THE ARMIES

Each player must first muster an army from their collection. A player can include any models in their army, but this mission is most suited to armies that contain numerous units of **Infantry** and few, if any, **Aircraft** and **Titanic** units. If a player's army is Battle-forged they will also be able to use the appropriate Stratagems included with this mission (see opposite). Once the armies have been chosen, the players must decide who will be the Attacker and who will be the Defender.

THE BATTLEFIELD

Create the battlefield using the deployment map below and set up terrain. There should be cover across the battlefield, in particular within the Defender's deployment zone. There should then be line of sight blocking terrain and other forms of cover across the battlefield, in particular within the Attacker's deployment zone.

DEPLOYMENT

The Defender deploys their army wholly within their deployment zone. The Attacker does not deploy their army. At the end of their first Movement phase, they set up their army as reinforcements wholly within their deployment zone. Any **Vehicle** units from their army must be set up wholly within 12" of the Attacker's battlefield edge.

FIRST TURN

The Attacker has the first turn.

DELAYED REINFORCEMENTS

Any of the Defender's units not set up on the battlefield during deployment cannot be set up in the first battle round, and such a unit can only be set up in the second battle round on a D6 roll of 4+. They can be set up as normal from the third and subsequent battle rounds.

MERCILESS AMBUSH

In the first battle round, when resolving an attack made with a ranged weapon against a unit from the Attacker's army that is wholly within 1" of a terrain feature, subtract 1 from the hit roll. In the first battle round, models in the Defender's army cannot be set up or finish any kind of move more than 12" away from the Defender's deployment zone.

LOST MOMENTUM

At the start of the battle round, the Attacker loses momentum as follows:

- Third and subsequent battle rounds: Each time the Attacker wishes to use a Stratagem, they must spend one additional Command Point to use that Stratagem.
- Fourth and subsequent battle rounds: Models in the Attacker's army cannot be affected by the aura abilities of friendly models.
- Fifth battle round: When resolving an attack made by a model in the Attacker's army, subtract 1 from the hit roll.

BATTLE LENGTH

The battle automatically ends at the end of battle round 5.

VICTORY CONDITIONS

No Mercy: At the end of each battle round, a player scores 1 victory point if more units from their opponent's army were destroyed in that battle round than were destroyed from their own army in that battle round.

No Respite: At the end of the battle, each player adds up the total Power Rating or points value (using whichever method was used to build your army) of destroyed units from their army. The player with the lowest total scores 1 victory point.

Iron Resolve: At the end of the battle, the Defender scores 1 victory point if any units from their army are on the battlefield.

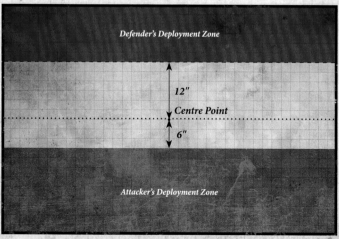

Defender's Battlefield Edge

Defender's Deployment Zone

12"

Centre Point

6"

Attacker's Deployment Zone

Attacker's Battlefield Edge

STRATAGEMS

In this mission, the players can use Command Points (CPs) to use the following bonus Stratagems:

DARING AMBUSH
1/2CP

Attacker Stratagem

With the enemy in sight, the ambushers rush forward to encircle their prey.

Use this Stratagem at the end of your first Movement phase. Select one **INFANTRY**, **BEAST** or **SWARM** unit from your army for 1CP, or two such units for 2CP. Those units can immediately move and can Advance, even though they were set up as reinforcements this turn. Those units must end that move more than 9" away from any enemy models.

RIGGED TRAP
2CP

Attacker Stratagem

Hidden explosives, psychic detonators or ravenous bio-vectors savage the enemy before a shot has been fired.

Use this Stratagem at the start of the first battle round, but before the first turn begins. Select one enemy unit on the battlefield that is not a **CHARACTER**. That unit suffers D3 mortal wounds. Roll one D6 for each other unit within 3" of that unit. On a 3+ that other unit suffers D3 mortal wounds. Until the start of the next battle round, halve the Move characteristic of any unit that suffered mortal wounds as a result of this Stratagem.

FIERCE ASSAULT
1CP

Attacker Stratagem

The carefully orchestrated hunt comes to a violent crescendo as the stalkers close upon their foe.

Use this Stratagem in your Shooting phase or the Fight phase, when a unit from your army is chosen to shoot or fight with. Until the end of that phase, when resolving an attack made by a model in that unit against the closest enemy unit, add 1 to the wound roll.

COUNTER-ATTACK
1CP

Defender Stratagem

Surrounded and caught off guard, warriors rally together to bring the fight to their enemy.

Use this Stratagem at the end of your opponent's Charge phase. Select one unit from your army. If there are any enemy units within 6" of that unit, it can perform a Heroic Intervention as if it were a **CHARACTER**, and can move up to 6" when doing so.

HEROIC LEADERSHIP
1CP

Defender Stratagem

It is only in the crucible of battle that commanders of great renown are forged.

Use this Stratagem during deployment, when you deploy a **CHARACTER** unit from your army. Add 3" to the range of that unit's aura abilities. You can only use this Stratagem once.

TAKE COVER
1CP

Defender Stratagem

When caught in the open, hillocks of rubble and the corpses of the dead can provide some measure of cover.

Use this Stratagem in any phase when a unit from your army within your deployment zone is chosen as the target of an attack. Until the end of that turn, that unit is treated as having the benefit of cover to its saving throw unless it has the **AIRCRAFT** or **TITANIC** keywords.

CRUCIBLE OF WAR
HOSTILE ACQUISITIONS

For the canny commander, the battlefield presents a wealth of strategic resources to be seized. Some armies may concentrate on sites of tactical importance or stockpiles of valuable materiel. Then again, to some the plundered minds and dissected flesh of enemy heroes possess a worth all of its own…

THE ARMIES

Each player must first muster an army from their collection. A player can include any models in their army, but this mission is most suited to armies that contain numerous units of **INFANTRY** and few, if any, **AIRCRAFT** and **TITANIC** units. If a player's army is Battle-forged, they will also be able to use the appropriate Stratagems included with this mission (see opposite). Once the armies have been chosen, the players must then decide who will be the Attacker and who will be the Defender.

THE BATTLEFIELD

Create the battlefield using the deployment map below and set up terrain. If possible, there should be a ruin or building that each of the objective markers can be set up in, or on.

DEPLOYMENT

The Defender sets up each of their **CHARACTER** units wholly within their deployment zone and more than 9" from any battlefield edge. **CHARACTER** units from the Defender's army must be set up on the battlefield in this way, and cannot be set up in any other locations. The Attacker then sets up their army, wholly within their deployment zone. Once the Attacker has finished setting up, the Defender sets up their remaining units, wholly within their deployment zone.

FIRST TURN

The Attacker has the first turn.

TAKEN ALIVE

If a **CHARACTER** unit from the Defender's army is destroyed by an attack made with a melee weapon, instead of removing that model from the battlefield, the Attacker can choose to place it next to the unit that made that attack. If they do so, that model is said to have been captured by that unit. It is no longer treated as a unit, but as a marker instead. If the model would impede the movement of any other models, simply move it out of the way. If the unit that has captured that **CHARACTER** is destroyed, the marker is removed, and that model is no longer said to have been captured.

BATTLE LENGTH

The battle automatically ends at the end of battle round 5.

VICTORY CONDITIONS

Vital Supplies: At the end of each battle round, a player scores 1 victory point if they control more objective markers than their opponent.

Captured Commanders: At the end of the battle, the Attacker scores 1 victory point for each enemy **CHARACTER** that is captured by one of their units.

Hold the Line: At the end of the battle, the Defender scores 1 victory point for each objective marker they control.

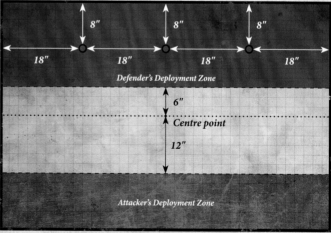

● *Objective Marker*

Defender's Battlefield Edge

8" 8" 8"

18" 18" 18" 18"

Defender's Deployment Zone

6"

Centre point

12"

Attacker's Deployment Zone

Attacker's Battlefield Edge

STRATAGEMS

In this mission, the players can use Command Points (CPs) to use the following bonus Stratagems:

1CP — SIPHON MATERIALS
Attacker Stratagem
Accompanied by non-combatant thralls and menials, these fighters know they can push onto the next objective while their subordinates concentrate on stealing supplies.

Use this Stratagem at the end of any battle round. Select one objective marker that you control. Until your opponent controls it, treat that objective marker as if 2 models in your army were within 3" of it.

1CP — FREED FROM THEIR BONDS
Defender Stratagem
Seeing their leaders carried away, some warriors will throw themselves into the fray to free them, heedless of any danger to themselves.

Use this Stratagem in your Charge phase when a unit from your army ends a charge move within 1" of an enemy unit that has any captured CHARACTER markers. Roll one D6 for each of those captured CHARACTER markers. On a 4+ that marker is removed.

2CP — ADVANCE SCOUTS
Attacker Stratagem
These forces have ranged ahead of the main force, locating the objectives and allowing the rest of the army to sweep in with precise intel.

Use this Stratagem during deployment, when you set up a unit from your army that has a Power Rating of 5 or less. That unit can be set up anywhere on the battlefield that is more than 9" away from the Defender's deployment zone, instead of wholly within the Attacker's deployment zone.

1CP — DETERMINED DEFENCE
Defender Stratagem
Through rousing oratory, grit and determination, these warriors will die rather than let the enemy capture this area.

Use this Stratagem at the start of the Morale phase. Select one unit from your army that is within 3" of any objective markers. When a Morale test is taken for this unit, do not roll the dice; it is automatically passed.

2CP — SEIZE SUPPLIES
Attacker Stratagem
In the event of a deadlock, your warriors grit their teeth and push the enemy back, however temporarily.

Use this Stratagem at the end of any battle round if you and your opponent both control the same number of objective markers. You are treated as controlling more objective markers than your opponent this battle round for the purposes of the Vital Supplies victory condition.

3CP — EVACUATE SUPPLIES
Defender Stratagem
Your forces have a supply of transport vehicles on hand to move these supplies to a new location should they come under heavy assault, assuming you can hold the foe long enough for them to be loaded.

Use this Stratagem at the end of any battle round. Select an objective marker that you control. If you still control that objective marker at the end of the next battle round, you can remove that objective marker from the battlefield. If you do so, that objective marker cannot be controlled at the end of any subsequent battle rounds, but at the end of the battle, your army is treated as controlling it for the purposes of the Hold the Line victory condition.

CRUCIBLE OF WAR
UNEXPECTED QUARTERS

The enemy have overrun your defences. The only thing left to do is to sacrifice your troops to buy you time to evacuate. However, as you make your way from the battle, another force unexpectedly arrives to cut off your escape…

THE ARMIES

This mission can be played with two or three players. One player will be the Defender. Another player will be the Attacker. If there is a third player, that player will be the Assassin. Otherwise, the Attacker will control a second force as the Assassin. Each player must muster an army from their collection. The Assassin should control a force that is approximately half the Power Level of that controlled by the Defender. If a player's army is Battle-forged, they will also be able to use the appropriate Stratagems included with this mission (see opposite).

THE BATTLEFIELD

Create the battlefield using the deployment map below and set up terrain. There should be more terrain features in the Defender's deployment zone than there are in the other half of the battlefield.

DEPLOYMENT

The Defender sets up their Warlord wholly within the Warlord's deployment zone. The Attacker and Defender then alternate setting up units, wholly within their own deployment zones. The Assassin's army is not set up on the battlefield, but if they have any units that can be set up in other locations (teleportariums, in the sky, in the webway etc.) they can declare which of their units will be set up in these locations.

FIRST TURN

The Assassin has the first turn, followed by the Attacker, then the Defender.

ASSASSINATION FORCE

At the end of their second and each subsequent Assassin's Movement phase, the Assassin player can roll one D6 for each unit in their army; on a 4+ that unit can be set up on the battlefield, anywhere within 6" of the Assassin's battlefield edge and more than 1" from any enemy models.

ESCAPE!

The Defender's Warlord must try to escape the battlefield. To do this, at the end of the third or subsequent battle round, that model must be within 1" of the Assassin's battlefield edge. If it is, the Warlord model is removed from that battlefield. It is then said to have escaped.

BATTLE LENGTH

The battle automatically ends at the end of battle round 5.

VICTORY CONDITIONS

The Attacker wins if the Defender's Warlord is destroyed by an attack made by one of their models or a psychic power manifested by one of their **PSYKERS**.

The Assassin wins if the Defender's Warlord is destroyed by an attack made by one of their models or a psychic power manifested by one of their **PSYKERS**.

The Defender wins if their Warlord has escaped at the end of the battle.

If the Defender's Warlord is destroyed by anything other than an attack made by one of the Attacker's or Assassin's models or a psychic power manifested by one of the Attacker's or Assassin's **PSYKERS**, the Assassin and Attacker draw and the Defender loses.

If the Defender's Warlord has not been destroyed and has not escaped at the end of the battle, the game is a draw.

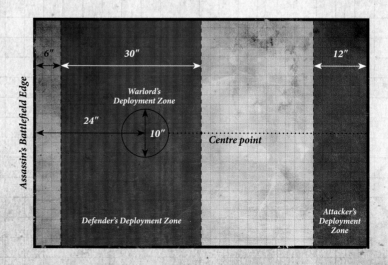

STRATAGEMS

In this mission, the players can use Command Points (CPs) to use the following bonus Stratagems:

ASSASSIN SHOT
1CP

Assassin Stratagem

Some warriors wait a lifetime for that one perfect shot, where it seems as if the whole flow of battle has placed the target in your sights.

Use this Stratagem in your Shooting phase when you select a model to attack with a ranged weapon. That model can only attack with one ranged weapon they are armed with in this phase, and can only make one attack with that weapon, but can ignore all other enemy units for the purposes of targeting CHARACTERS.

LOCATION TRIANGULATED
1CP

Assassin Stratagem

Now that the location of the target has been ascertained, the full power of your strike force can be brought to bear.

Use this Stratagem at the end of your Charge phase if a unit from your army is within 1" of the Defender's Warlord. Select one unit from your army that has not yet been set up on the battlefield. Set that unit up on the battlefield anywhere that is within 6" of the Assassin's battlefield edge and more than 1" from any enemy models.

GET TO THE TARGET
2CP

Attacker Stratagem

Your warriors must get to the target at any cost. Whether by athletic means or pure power, nothing will stand in their way.

Use this Stratagem in your Charge phase when you declare the Defender's Warlord as the target of a charge by a unit from your army. Until the end of that phase, the charging unit can move over enemy units as if they can FLY.

RAPID ASSAULT
2CP

Attacker Stratagem

Your forces are making all speed for the objective, its elimination all that matters at this point in the battle.

Use this Stratagem at the start of your Shooting phase. Select one unit from your army that Advanced this turn. Until the end of that phase, you can shoot with that unit as if it had not Advanced.

OUT OF SIGHT
3CP

Defender Stratagem

Sometimes, when fleeing for your life, you just need to get into cover and re-evaluate your options.

Use this Stratagem at the end of your Movement phase if your Warlord is wholly within a terrain feature. Until your next Movement phase, your Warlord cannot make attacks with ranged weapons, but cannot be selected as the target of an attack made with a ranged weapon by an enemy model.

PROTECT YOUR COMMANDER!
1CP

Defender Stratagem

Sometimes an inspirational word is all that is required to convince your subordinates to sacrifice their lives to save yours.

Use this Stratagem at the start of your opponent's Shooting or Fight phase. Until the end of that phase, each time your Warlord would lose any wounds as a result of an attack made against that Warlord's unit, you can select a unit from your army that is within 3" of your Warlord and roll one D6. On a 4+ that model does not lose those wounds and the selected unit suffers 1 mortal wound for each of those wounds. Only one attempt can be made to intercept each attack.

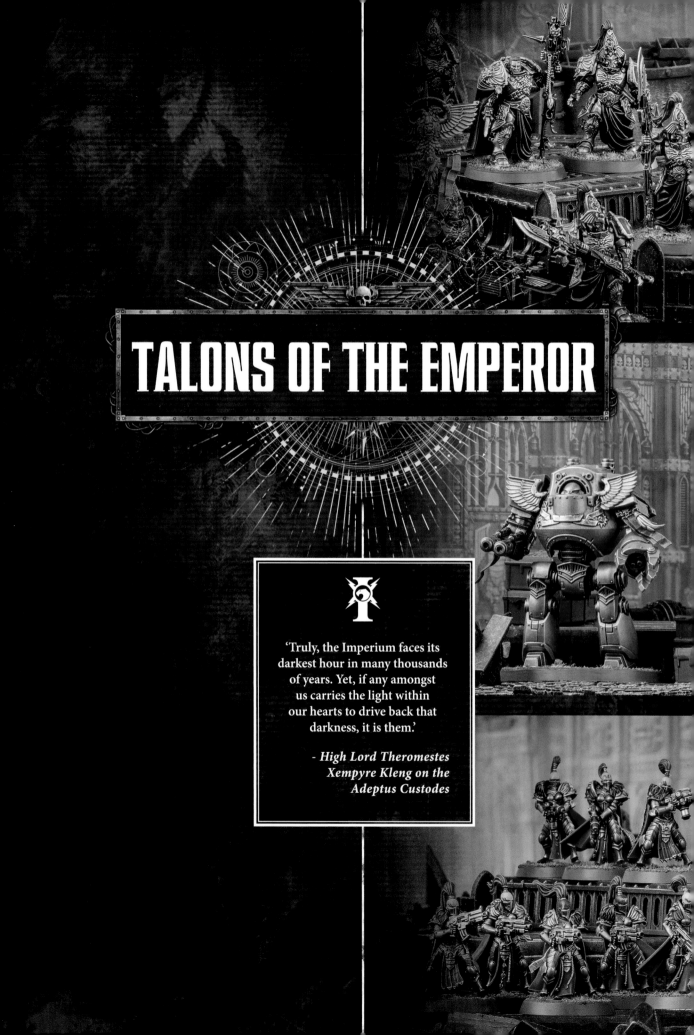

TALONS OF THE EMPEROR

'Truly, the Imperium faces its darkest hour in many thousands of years. Yet, if any amongst us carries the light within our hearts to drive back that darkness, it is them.'

- High Lord Theromestes Xempyre Kleng on the Adeptus Custodes

THE TEN THOUSAND

The rules in this section supplement those found in *Codex: Adeptus Custodes* and can be used in any open play, narrative play or matched play game. With them, you will be able to forge your brotherhood of legendary heroes into a shield host trained in specialised ways of war and wielding ancient Terran relics.

This section is a supplement to *Codex: Adeptus Custodes* – you will need a copy of that book to use the rules in this section.

This section contains Relics, Warlord Traits and Stratagems to allow you to field a force representing specific shield hosts of the Adeptus Custodes. You will also find additional Stratagems that can be used with any Adeptus Custodes army, a Stratagem that can be used to upgrade your **SHIELD-CAPTAIN** with an additional rule to represent the leader of a shield host, and a name generator with which you can personalise your characters.

'The hotter the forge the finer the blade, or so they say. The forge of war in which we now find ourselves blazes hotter than anything the Imperium has seen in ten millennia. We, of the Adeptus Custodes, were built to endure these fires. They will not be our end. Instead, we will be honed to the finest cutting edge that we may be the bane of even the foulest of heretics.'

- Captain-General Trajann Valoris

SHIELD HOSTS

Multiple shield companies gather into larger forces known as shield hosts in times of dire need. Sometimes boasting hundreds of Custodians, shield hosts possess tremendous martial might. The greatest of them have long and established histories, unified heraldry and duties uniquely theirs to discharge.

If your army is Battle-forged and includes any **ADEPTUS CUSTODES** Detachments, you can select which shield host each of those Detachments belongs to from the shield hosts listed on the following pages. If you do, all **ADEPTUS CUSTODES** units from that Detachment (excluding Captain-General Trajann Valoris) gain the relevant <**SHIELD HOST**> Faction keyword.

For example, if your army includes an **ADEPTUS CUSTODES** Detachment containing a Shield-Captain, Captain-General Trajann Valoris and three units of Custodian Guard, and you decide that Detachment is from the Shadowkeepers, those units (excluding Captain-General Trajann Valoris) would gain the **SHADOWKEEPERS** Faction keyword.

An **ADEPTUS CUSTODES** Detachment that belongs to one of the shield hosts has access to the following rules:

RELICS OF TERRA

If your army is led by an **ADEPTUS CUSTODES** <**SHIELD HOST**> Warlord, you can give the relevant <**SHIELD HOST**> Relic of Terra to an **ADEPTUS CUSTODES** <**SHIELD HOST**> **CHARACTER** model from your army, instead of one from *Codex: Adeptus Custodes*. Note that named characters cannot be given a Relic of Terra.

Note that some Relics are weapons or items of wargear that replace one of the model's existing weapons or items of wargear. Where this is the case, you must, if you are using points values, still pay the cost of the weapon or wargear that is being replaced. Write down any Relics your models have on your army roster.

WARLORD TRAITS

If an **ADEPTUS CUSTODES** <**SHIELD HOST**> model is your Warlord, they can have the relevant <**SHIELD HOST**> Warlord Trait instead of a Warlord Trait from *Codex: Adeptus Custodes* or another publication.

STRATAGEMS

If your army is Battle-forged and includes any **ADEPTUS CUSTODES** <**SHIELD HOST**> Detachments, the relevant <**SHIELD HOST**> Stratagem can be used in addition to those presented in this publication and in *Codex: Adeptus Custodes*.

SHADOWKEEPERS

The Shadowkeepers watch over the Dark Cells beneath the Imperial Palace and keep trammelled the dread entities and technologies sealed within. Should such potent and terrible manifestations appear abroad in the Imperium, it falls to the Shadowkeepers to capture and imprison them.

WARLORD TRAIT: LOCKWARDEN

The master of the Shadowkeepers is the Lockwarden, an especially stern guardian. He must be implacable in defence and unrelenting on the attack, a master gaoler feared by all his charges.

When resolving an attack made by a **CHARACTER** model against this Warlord, subtract 1 from the hit roll. When resolving an attack made by this Warlord against an enemy **CHARACTER** unit, subtract 1 from the saving throw (including invulnerable saves).

RELIC OF TERRA: STASIS OUBLIETTE

This unassuming, rune-inscribed piece of arcane technology entraps its victim in a shimmering stasis prison for capture and return to Terra.

At the start of the Fight phase, select one enemy **CHARACTER** unit within 3" of a model with this Relic. Until the end of that phase, halve the Attacks characteristic of models in that unit (rounding up) and when resolving an attack made by a friendly **SHADOWKEEPERS** model against that **CHARACTER** unit, re-roll a wound roll of 1.

1CP

GRIM RESPONSIBILITY
Shadowkeepers Stratagem

The Shadowkeepers' role requires superhuman resolve and a fortitude of will so unbreakable that it is like unto a monolithic fortress. When set to their task, the Shadowkeepers shrug off the worst that their foes can throw at them, ignoring the sorest wounds through sheer force of determination. For their already outmatched enemies, it is a terrifying spectacle.

Use this Stratagem in any phase when a **SHADOWKEEPERS** unit from your army is chosen as the target of an attack. Until the end of that phase, when resolving an attack against that unit, subtract 1 from the Strength characteristic of that attack.

AQUILAN SHIELD

Certain servants of the Emperor bear great responsibilities deemed directly relevant to the safety of Terra. Such esteemed figures are afforded the protection of the Aquilan Shield, at least until their usefulness is thought to be at its end. Bodyguards and protectors without equal, these warriors devote every iota of their strength and will to the defence of their assigned charge, be that an Indomitus Crusade Fleetmaster or a lowly Astra Militarum Guardsman turned visionary prophet.

WARLORD TRAIT: REVERED COMPANION

Years of interposing himself between his charges and the blades of their foes has left this warlord adept at turning and deflecting attacks.

When resolving an attack made against this Warlord, halve any damage inflicted (rounding up).

RELIC OF TERRA: PRAESIDIUS

Fashioned by the great Terran armourer Annah Tsvochakin in the latter years of M32, the stunningly worked storm shield named Praesidius is a singular artefact. Not only is its auramite surface finely worked and layered at a molecular level for greater durability, but nestled within its graven bulk are a series of micro-shield generators. Employing a never again replicated modification of displacer technology, the shield generates small localised displacement bubbles at the point of impact, literally beaming bolts, bullets and the tips of blades harmlessly away from Praesidius' bearer.

Model with a storm shield only. When resolving an attack against a model with this Relic, subtract 1 from the wound roll.

DREAD HOST

Fear is a familiar weapon to the Imperium, used to deter enemies and keep seething populations in line. There is no terror as pure and absolute as that invoked when the Emperor's own fury is unleashed to punish his foes. Such is the Dread Host, a weapon forged to strike at dawning threats and spread terror through absolute annihilation.

WARLORD TRAIT: ALL-SEEING ANNIHILATOR

The Dread Host employ a near-prescient intelligence network to foresee their enemies' plans and weaknesses. This warlord employs that amassed knowledge to best direct his comrades' attacks.

When resolving an attack made with a melee weapon by a model in a friendly **DREAD HOST** unit within 6" of this Warlord, an unmodified hit roll of 6 scores 1 additional hit.

RELIC OF TERRA: ADMONIMORTIS

This towering castellan axe was wrought for one purpose – to make a bloody example of those who dare to set themselves against the inviolate might of Terra.

Model with a castellan axe only. This Relic of Terra replaces a castellan axe and has the following profile:

WEAPON	RANGE	TYPE	S	AP	D
Admonimortis (shooting)	24"	Rapid Fire 1	4	-1	2
Admonimortis (melee)	Melee	Melee	+3	-3	3

1CP
SHIELD OF HONOUR
Aquilan Shield Stratagem

It is second nature to the warriors of the Aquilan Shield to place themselves between their charges and potential peril.

Use this Stratagem in any phase when an **IMPERIUM CHARACTER** unit from your army is chosen as the target of an attack made by a model in an enemy unit. Select one friendly **AQUILAN SHIELD INFANTRY** or **AQUILAN SHIELD DREADNOUGHT** unit within 3" of that **IMPERIUM CHARACTER** unit. Until the end of that phase, when resolving an attack made by a model in that enemy unit, measure range to that **IMPERIUM CHARACTER** unit, but resolve attacks made by models in that enemy model's unit against the unit you selected. If the unit you selected is destroyed, any remaining attacks are lost.

1/2CP
GOLDEN LIGHT OF THE MOIRAIDES
Dread Host Stratagem

The Dread Host go to battle aboard the trio of terrifying pre-heresy warships known as the Moiraides. These potent vessels teleport their passengers straight into battle, their systems so precise that the Adeptus Custodes can begin their charge aboard their warship and complete it by surging at a full run from an explosion of golden light in the enemy's midst.

Use this Stratagem at the start of your Charge phase. Select one **DREAD HOST** unit from your army that teleported into battle this turn for 1CP, or up to three such units for 2CP. Until the end of that phase, when a charge roll is made for those units, roll one additional D6 and discard one of the dice.

SOLAR WATCH

The Solar Watch move fast and strike hard, launching their Talon Sorties to eliminate those threats in or around the Sol System itself. Their wrath is swift and terrible, delivered with a martial precision that few could match.

WARLORD TRAIT: SALLY FORTH

This warlord excels in directing fast and deadly offensives designed to close rapidly with the enemy, then overwhelm them with a devastating concentration of force.

At the start of your Movement phase, add 1" to the Move characteristic of all friendly **SOLAR WATCH** units within 6" of this Warlord until the end of that phase. Whilst their unit is within 6" of this Warlord, models in friendly **SOLAR WATCH** units that have Advanced can shoot with Rapid Fire weapons in the following Shooting phase, but must subtract 1 from hit rolls for those attacks.

RELIC OF TERRA: THE SWIFTSILVER TALON

Perfectly balanced, wrought from lightweight zephyrgeldt alloys, this remarkable spear is also imbued with a ferociously predatory and quick-thinking machine spirit.

Model with a Guardian Spear only. A model with this Relic can shoot and charge in a turn in which it Advanced or Fell Back. This Relic of Terra replaces a Guardian Spear and has the following profile:

WEAPON	RANGE	TYPE	S	AP	D
Swiftsilver Talon (shooting)	24"	Assault 4	4	-1	2
Swiftsilver Talon (melee)	Melee	Melee	+1	-3	D3

EMISSARIES IMPERATUS

In the days of the Great Crusade, the Emperor often entrusted crucial messages or artefacts to be borne by his Custodians. It is a duty they still fulfil now, speaking, acting and making war with the absolute authority of the Master of Mankind himself.

WARLORD TRAIT: VOICE OF THE EMPEROR

Where many amongst the Adeptus Custodes hold themselves remote and aloof from the lesser mortals around them, this warlord's booming oratory and inspirational rhetoric are meant for the ears and hearts of all loyal Imperial servants.

Whilst they are within 9" of this Warlord, friendly **IMPERIUM** units can use this Warlord's Leadership characteristic. Add 3" to the range of this Warlord's aura abilities (this has already been added to this trait's aura ability).

RELIC OF TERRA: VEXILLA DOMINATUS

The Vexilla Dominatus blazes with an arcane light that illuminates the battlefield like the rays of Sol itself. Bathed in such blessed radiance, the Emperor's servants stand tall indeed.

Model with a Vexilla Defensor only. Replace a model with this Relic's Custodes Vexilla and Vexilla Defensor ability with the following:

Vexilla Dominatus: Whilst they are within 6" of a model with this Relic, you can re-roll failed Morale tests for friendly **IMPERIUM INFANTRY** and **IMPERIUM BIKER** units. Whilst their unit is within 6" of a model with this Relic, friendly **EMISSARIES IMPERATUS** models count as 3 models for the purposes of determining who controls an objective marker.

THE EAGLE'S STRIKE
0CP

Solar Watch Stratagem

When the Solar Watch attack they prioritise the speedy elimination of their foes' command assets, swooping like a great eagle and tearing the throat from the enemy army with talons and beak. The foe are left reeling and confused, their command structure collapsing even as the Solar Watch ready themselves to strike the killing blow.

Use this Stratagem in any phase when an enemy **CHARACTER** unit is destroyed as a result of an attack made by a **SOLAR WATCH** model from your army. The next time your opponent wishes to use a Stratagem, they must spend one extra CP to use that Stratagem. This Stratagem can be used once per battle round.

THE EMPEROR'S HAND
1CP

Emissaries Imperatus Stratagem

Most Custodians who join the Emissaries Imperatus do so because they profess to see visions of the Emperor guiding them in their dreams. Some even find that this guidance flows through into their waking hours. They claim to feel the Emperor's own hands upon their weapons and voice in their minds, exposing the weaknesses of their foes.

Use this Stratagem in any phase when an **EMISSARIES IMPERATUS** unit from your army is chosen to shoot or fight with. Until the end of that phase, when resolving an attack made by a model in that unit, ignore any negative hit roll, wound roll and Armour Penetration characteristic modifiers and any benefit to the saving throw as a result of cover for that attack.

ADEPTUS CUSTODES STRATAGEMS

If your army is Battle-forged and includes any ADEPTUS CUSTODES Detachments (excluding Auxiliary Support Detachments), you have access to the Stratagems shown over the following pages and can spend Command Points to activate them. These reflect the unique strategies used by the Adeptus Custodes. If a Stratagem is used before the battle to upgrade a unit (e.g. Ten Thousand Heroes) and you have an army roster, you must note on it which Stratagems are used to upgrade which units.

1CP · TEN THOUSAND HEROES
Adeptus Custodes Stratagem

Every Custodian Guard is a storied hero; many amongst the ranks of their shield companies possess the most advanced mastery of war.

Use this Stratagem before the battle, after nominating your Warlord. Select one ADEPTUS CUSTODES CHARACTER model from your army that is not your Warlord and determine one Warlord Trait for it; it is regarded as your Warlord for the purposes of that Warlord Trait. Each Warlord Trait in your army must be unique (if randomly generated, re-roll duplicate results). You can only use this Stratagem once per battle.

1CP · ANCIENT ARTIFICE
Adeptus Custodes Stratagem

The secrets of manufacturing Contemptor Dreadnought sarcophagi are long lost, but no less potent for it.

Use this Stratagem in any phase, when an ADEPTUS CUSTODES DREADNOUGHT unit from your army is chosen as the target for an attack. Until the end of that phase, when resolving an attack made against that unit, halve the damage inflicted (rounding up).

2CP · ARCANE GENETIC ALCHEMY
Adeptus Custodes Stratagem

The Adeptus Custodes are individually engineered on a molecular level using secrets of genetic alchemy that render them virtual demigods in battle.

Use this Stratagem in any phase, when an ADEPTUS CUSTODES unit from your army that is not a VEHICLE is chosen as a target for an attack. Until the end of that phase, when resolving an attack made against that unit, an unmodified wound roll of 1-3 always fails, irrespective of any abilities that the weapon or the model making that attack has.

1CP · ETERNAL PENITENT
Adeptus Custodes Stratagem

Custodians tainted by dishonour seek penance through voluntary entombment in a Dreadnought's sarcophagus.

Use this Stratagem before the battle. Select one ADEPTUS CUSTODES DREADNOUGHT unit from your army. Increase that unit's Attacks characteristic by 1. You can re-roll charge rolls made for that unit. Each ADEPTUS CUSTODES DREADNOUGHT unit from your army can only be selected for this Stratagem once.

2CP · VENGEANCE OF THE MACHINE SPIRIT
Adeptus Custodes Stratagem

Not easily are the war engines of the Adeptus Custodes slain, and even then they do not pass quietly.

Use this Stratagem in any phase, when an ADEPTUS CUSTODES VEHICLE model from your army with the Power of the Machine Spirit ability is destroyed. That model can either automatically explode (do not roll a D6), shoot with one of its ranged weapons as if it were your Shooting phase, or make one attack with one of its melee weapons as if it were the Fight phase (use the top row of that model's damage table when shooting with that ranged weapon or resolving that attack with a melee weapon).

2CP · SLAYERS OF NIGHTMARES
Adeptus Custodes Stratagem

In an age plagued by monstrous foes, when primordial horrors from the darkest void circle Humanity's dying light, still the Adeptus Custodes stand strong!

Use this Stratagem in the Fight phase, when an ADEPTUS CUSTODES unit from your army is chosen to fight with. Until the end of that phase, when resolving an attack made with a melee weapon by a model in that unit against a unit with a higher Toughness characteristic than its own, you can add 1 to the wound roll.

FORTRESS OF WILLPOWER
1CP

Adeptus Custodes Stratagem

Unclean tendrils of witchcraft slither in futile frustration across the indomitable souls of the Adeptus Custodes, never finding a single crack to give them purchase.

Use this Stratagem in your opponent's Psychic phase, when an **ADEPTUS CUSTODES** unit from your army is selected as the target of a Psychic power that was successfully manifested this turn. Roll one D6, adding 1 to the result if that unit is a **CUSTODIAN WARDENS** unit; on a 4+ that psychic power has no effect.

BLOOD GAMES VETERANS
1/2CP

Adeptus Custodes Stratagem

What better way to defend one's master against assassins than to be one's self a masterful assassin?

Use this Stratagem in your Shooting phase. Select one **ADEPTUS CUSTODES** unit from your army that contains five or less models for 1CP or six or more models for 2CP. Until the end of that phase, when resolving an attack made with a ranged weapon by a model in that unit, an unmodified hit roll of 6 automatically scores a hit and successfully wounds the target (do not make a wound roll).

INDOMITABLE ENGINES
1CP

Adeptus Custodes Stratagem

So indomitable are the war engines of the Adeptus Custodes that they can shrug off even the most devastating hits without any obvious harm.

Use this Stratagem in any phase, when an **ADEPTUS CUSTODES VEHICLE** model from your army would lose a wound as a result of a mortal wound. Roll one D6; on a 5+ that wound is not lost. In addition, until the end of that phase, when this model would lose a wound as a result of a mortal wound, roll one D6; on a 5+ that wound is not lost.

ARCHEOTECH MUNITIONS
1CP

Adeptus Custodes Stratagem

The Adeptus Custodes have access to stockpiles of ancient and incredibly rare weaponry and ammunition.

Use this Stratagem in your Shooting phase, when an **ADEPTUS CUSTODES** unit from your army is chosen to shoot with. Until the end of that phase, when resolving an attack made with a ranged weapon with a Damage characteristic of D6 by a model in that unit, roll one additional D6 and discard one of the dice.

SUPERIOR FIRE PATTERNS
1CP

Adeptus Custodes Stratagem

Combining advanced targeting cogitators and their own sublimely honed reactions, the Custodians lay down a hail of fire worthy of an army many times their number.

Use this Stratagem in your Shooting phase, when an **ADEPTUS CUSTODES INFANTRY** unit from your army that did not Advance in your previous Movement phase is chosen to shoot with. Until the end of that phase, models in that unit make double the number of attacks with Rapid Fire and Pistol weapons.

AURAMITE AND ADAMANTIUM
1CP

Adeptus Custodes Stratagem

Allarus Custodians have been known to stride unharmed from the blasts of anti-Titan weapons.

Use this Stratagem in any phase, when an **ADEPTUS CUSTODES TERMINATOR** unit from your army is selected as the target of an attack. Until the end of that phase, when resolving an attack against that unit, an Armour Penetration characteristic of -1 or -2 is resolved as 0 for that attack.

THE EMPEROR'S AUSPICE
2CP

Adeptus Custodes Stratagem

When the eye of the Emperor is upon his champions, no foul trickery of the foe can prevail.

Use this Stratagem in any phase, when an **ADEPTUS CUSTODES** unit from your army is chosen as the target of an attack. Until the end of that phase, when resolving an attack against that unit, your opponent cannot re-roll any dice for that attack.

FRATERNITY OF HEROES
1CP

Adeptus Custodes Stratagem

Any Custodian would place himself in peril to protect his brothers without a moment's hesitation.

Use this Stratagem at the end of your opponent's Charge phase. Select one **ADEPTUS CUSTODES** unit from your army more than 1" away from any enemy models. That unit can immediately perform a Heroic Intervention as if it were a **CHARACTER**, but must finish that move within 1" of one or more enemy units.

LORDS OF THE SHIELD HOSTS

Those who command the Shield Hosts in battle are inhumanly skilled warriors and commanders who have earned the eternal respect of their comrades through exemplary deeds beyond counting.

If your army is Battle-forged and includes any **ADEPTUS CUSTODES** Detachments (excluding Auxiliary Support Detachments), you have access to the Stratagem to the right and can spend Command Points to activate it. If you do so and you have an army roster, you must note on it which selection you have made for your Shield-Captain.

CAPTAIN-COMMANDER TRAITS

- **Slayer of the Unclean:** When resolving an attack made by this model, on an unmodified wound roll of 6, double the Damage characteristic of the weapon for that attack (e.g. D3 becomes 2D3).

- **Swift as the Eagle:** Add 1 to Advance and charge rolls made for this model. Add 1" to the Move characteristic of this model.

- **Strategic Mastermind:** Whilst this model is on the battlefield, you can roll one D6 for each Command Point you spend to use a Stratagem; on a 5+ that Command Point is refunded. You can only have 1 Command Point refunded per battle round by this ability.

- **Bane of Abominations:** When resolving an attack made by this model against an enemy **MONSTER** unit or **VEHICLE** unit, you can re-roll the wound roll.

- **Indomitable Constitution:** Add 2 to the Wounds characteristic of this model.

- **Master of Melee:** Whilst this model is within 1" of any enemy units that contain six or more models, increase its Attacks characteristic by 2.

- **Unstoppable Destroyer:** When this model piles in, it can move up to D3+3" and can end the move closer to any enemy model within that distance of this model. When this model consolidates, it can move up to D3+3" and does not have to end the move closer to the nearest enemy model.

- **Defiant to the Last:** For each wound this model has lost, increase its Attacks characteristic by 1 (to a maximum of 3 additional attacks).

- **Inspirational Exemplar:** Add 3" to the range of this model's aura abilities.

1CP

CAPTAIN-COMMANDER
Adeptus Custodes Stratagem

Though an honorific more than an official rank, those named Captain-Commander richly deserve the accolade for their martial and strategic mastery.

Use this Stratagem before the battle. Select one **SHIELD-CAPTAIN** model from your army that is not a named character. Select one Captain-Commander Trait from the list to the left for that model. You can only use this Stratagem once per battle.

ADEPTUS CUSTODES NAME GENERATOR

This section is a tool to help you forge the names of your Adeptus Custodes. If you wish to randomly generate a name for one of your Custodians, you can roll a D66 and consult one or both of the tables below. To roll a D66, simply roll two D6, one after the other – the first represents tens, and the second represents digits, giving you a result between 11 and 66. These names should be considered largely interchangeable in terms of their order, and for a Custodian you can roll up a string of as many names as you like!

D66	NAME	D66	NAME
11	Tybalus	11	Drund
12	Aetheus	12	Koumadra
13	Dalat	13	Calaxor
14	Kariyan	14	Uremedes
15	Basillaeus	15	Desh
16	Tristraen	16	Cassabar
21	Erasmian	21	D'essa
22	Heracal	22	Ganorth
23	Tauramacchis	23	Valorian
24	Nurthias	24	Bastoris
25	Hasturias	25	Daryth
26	Artoris	26	Ganyth
31	Nathadian	31	Gallimadean
32	Io	32	Ossian
33	Harkhas	33	Urdanesh
34	Constantin	34	Vadrian
35	Eratorius	35	Helsates
36	Archimallus	36	Maxin
41	Telchor	41	Constor
42	Kallisarian	42	Valdus
43	Lencilius	43	Tasolian
44	Darian	44	Steale
45	Lytanus	45	Thursk
46	Rothrian	46	Loque
51	Leotydus	51	Feldorus
52	Parradon	52	Tychor
53	Borsa	53	Ganestus
54	Alhoris	54	Desmondages
55	Yortar	55	Talorn
56	Sanash	56	Launceddre
61	Pydanoris	61	Calligus
62	Manastus	62	Cheim
63	Jaeharl	63	Lychansis
64	Heraclast	64	Dat-Hastael
65	Aesoth	65	Ghau
66	Tybaris	66	Uriaxes

CADRES OF THE SILENT SISTERS

This section provides rules for Sisters of Silence usable in any open play, narrative play or matched play game. These allow you to gather your cadres and unleash their specialised witch-seeking tactics upon the foe, either on their own or as part of a combined force with the Adeptus Custodes.

This section contains all of the datasheets and Stratagems that you will need in order to fight battles with your Sisters of Silence models. You will also find rules for including these models in your Adeptus Custodes and Imperium armies, and a name generator with which you can personalise your characters.

DATASHEETS

On pages 43-45 you will find background and datasheets for your Sisters of Silence units to use in games of Warhammer 40,000.

STRATAGEMS

If your army is Battle-forged and includes any **Sisters of Silence** Detachments (excluding Auxiliary Support Detachments), or any **Adeptus Custodes** Detachments that include any **Sisters of Silence** units, you can use the Stratagems on page 46.

NAME GENERATOR

On page 47 you will find a useful tool to help you name members of your Silent Sisterhood.

ABILITIES

The following abilities are common to many Sisters of Silence units:

WITCH HUNTERS

When resolving an attack made by a model in this unit against a **Psyker** unit, you can re-roll the wound roll.

PSYCHIC ABOMINATION

This unit cannot be targeted or affected by psychic powers. When a Psychic test or a Deny the Witch test is taken for an enemy model, subtract 1 from the total for each unit from your army with this ability within 18" of that model (to a maximum of -4).

BATTLE-FORGED ARMIES

TALONS OF THE EMPEROR

If your army is Battle-forged, units with the **Sisters of Silence** Faction keyword can be included in an **Adeptus Custodes** Detachment in your army, without preventing that Detachment from being an **Adeptus Custodes** Detachment. Note that this does not prevent **Adeptus Custodes** units in that Detachment from gaining any Detachment abilities (e.g. The Emperor's Chosen and the Sworn Guardians abilities), however **Sisters of Silence** units cannot themselves gain any Detachment abilities. Similarly, those **Sisters of Silence** units are ignored for any rules that state all units from that Detachment must have at least one Faction keyword in common (e.g. in a matched play game) and when determining your army's Faction.

NULL-MAIDENS

A **Sisters of Silence** Vanguard Detachment – that is, a Vanguard Detachment that includes only **Sisters of Silence** units – is treated as having HQ Battlefield Role slots of '0' and Command Benefits of 'None'. Note that this means there are no compulsory HQ selections for **Sisters of Silence** Vanguard Detachments.

POINTS VALUES

If you are playing a matched play game, or a game that uses a points limit, you can use the following to determine the points cost of your army. Simply add together the points costs of all your models to determine your army's total points value.

UNITS

UNIT	MODELS PER UNIT	POINTS PER MODEL (Excluding wargear)
Null-Maiden Rhino	1	65
Prosecutors	5-10	10
Vigilators	5-10	10
Witchseekers	5-10	10

RANGED WEAPONS

WEAPON	POINTS PER WEAPON
Boltgun	0
Flamer	6
Hunter-killer missile	6
Psyk-out grenades	0
Storm bolter	2

MELEE WEAPONS

WEAPON	POINTS PER WEAPON
Executioner greatblade	5

SISTERS OF SILENCE

In an age of dark sorcery and empyric cataclysm, the Sisters of Silence have never been more important to the Imperium. Each of these Null-Maidens is not only a lethally skilled warrior, but also a psychic blank, their very presence anathema to the deviant witches they hunt in the Emperor's name.

To the common herd of Humanity, those who bear the incredibly rare Pariah gene are known as nulls, blanks, untouchables or a raft of yet more vitriolic names. Such individuals have no presence at all in the warp; to all intents and purposes they possess nothing that could be called a soul. As a result of this strange condition, Pariahs are surrounded by an intense and unsettling aura that causes others to dislike, distrust and soon turn against them. Yet they also possess a substantial advantage for all their apparently cursed nature; the presence of even a single Null chokes off psykers' connection to the warp, while in turn those witches' malefic powers cannot affect the Null in the slightest.

In the Sisters of Silence, this ability finds potent martial application. They are witch-hunters and psyker-slayers without compare, working alone as part of their own Cadres or alongside other Imperial agents to track down and neutralise the most dangerous psychic witches. Human or xenos, it does not matter – once the Null-Maidens have their target surrounded, even its most monstrously powerful psychic abilities are rendered as impotent as its despairing screams. Indeed, the sudden severing of a witch's connection to the warp can prove a devastating weapon in its own right; for many practitioners, the effect is as disorientating and as distressing as being rendered suddenly deaf, dumb or blind.

The Null-Maidens do not rely upon this effect alone to win their battles, of course. Many psykers will still fight back with every weapon at their disposal, even while reeling from the trammelling of their mental gifts. Others surround themselves with heretical cults or devoted armies that must be hacked and blasted apart before the Sisters of Silence can reach their primary target. To this end, every Null-Maiden is a lethal warrior, clad in masterfully crafted armour and wielding an array of potent weaponry with superb skill. Even a single squad of Null-Maidens is more than a match for entire warbands of lesser warriors; when they deploy at Cadre strength, they have the martial might to cut the heart from a rogue psyker's benighted empire.

Every Null-Maiden is trained from a young age. They begin their progression as novices and advance to the status of a full-fledged Sister of Silence only once they have proven themselves worthy. It is at this point that they take the lifelong vow of silence, the Oath of Tranquility, that lends them their name. From this point onward they communicate with one another only through the use of Thoughtmark –a private and highly nuanced form of sign language – and Battlemark, its more declarative and robust battlefield cousin. Null-Maidens in battle thus make a truly unnerving spectacle, their Pariah's aura filling their enemies with dread, their lightning assaults carried out without a word spoken or a battle cry given voice. Only the thunder of their guns and the steely songs of their blades speak for the Sisters of Silence upon the battlefield, but these are more than voice enough.

Prosecutor Squads form the core of the Silent Sisters' armies, and they are lethal in both attack and defence. Wielding Umbra-pattern boltguns with terrifying precision, they lay down thunderous salvoes of perfectly placed bolt shells that blast witches and their heretical followers into bloody ruin. Where psykers congregate or employ their unclean powers to augment their followers rather than assailing the Prosecutors directly, the Null-Maidens hurl glittering psyk-out grenades that assail the warp-senses of their enemies and set them reeling amidst a vortex of confusion and despair.

Vigilator Squads, by comparison, embody the swift and deadly sword-strike that severs witch's heads from their necks and ends their threat at a stroke. Armed with heirloom blades wreathed in potent disruptor fields, Vigilators train tirelessly in an ancient sword form that lays open their victim's guard before ending the fight with a single, decapitating blow. Even a single such Null-Maiden is a terrifying enemy in one-on-one combat, but when an entire band of Vigilators fall upon a single heretic psyker or xenos abomination with their blades questing for its neck, its doom is swiftly sealed.

Witchseeker Squads wield fire as their primary weapon. Each bears a thrice-blessed flamer capable to belching sheets of blazing promethium that engulf their victims and reduce them to charnel ash. The Witchseekers coordinate their fire with eerie precision, overlapping their cones of flame to utterly eradicate their victims or sending out expertly placed tongues of fire that ignite the cover or defences behind which their targets cower. Witchseekers often work in concert with Prosecutor and Vigilator Squads, the former flushing their prey from cover before the latter pounce upon their blazing, shrieking victims and strike the killing blow.

PROSECUTORS

3 POWER

NAME	M	WS	BS	S	T	W	A	Ld	Sv
Prosecutor	7"	3+	3+	3	3	1	2	8	3+
Sister Superior	7"	3+	3+	3	3	1	3	9	3+

This unit contains 1 Sister Superior and 4 Prosecutors. It can additionally contain up to 5 Prosecutors (**Power Rating +3**). Each model is equipped with: boltgun; psyk-out grenades.

WEAPON	RANGE	TYPE	S	AP	D	ABILITIES
Boltgun	24"	Rapid Fire 1	4	0	1	-
Psyk-out grenades	6"	Grenade D3	2	0	1	When resolving an attack made with this weapon against a **PSYKER** or **DAEMON** unit, a hit roll of 6+ inflicts 1 mortal wound on the target and the attack sequence ends.

ABILITIES	Psychic Abomination, Witch Hunters (pg 42)
	Prosecution Protocols: Models in this unit can target enemy **CHARACTERS** that are **PSYKERS**, even if they are not the closest enemy unit.
FACTION KEYWORDS	**IMPERIUM, ASTRA TELEPATHICA, SISTERS OF SILENCE**
KEYWORDS	**INFANTRY, PROSECUTORS**

VIGILATORS

4 POWER

NAME	M	WS	BS	S	T	W	A	Ld	Sv
Vigilator	7"	3+	3+	3	3	1	2	8	3+
Sister Superior	7"	3+	3+	3	3	1	3	9	3+

This unit contains 1 Sister Superior and 4 Vigilators. It can additionally contain up to 5 Vigilators (**Power Rating +4**). Each model is equipped with: executioner greatblade; psyk-out grenades.

WEAPON	RANGE	TYPE	S	AP	D	ABILITIES
Executioner greatblade	Melee	Melee	+2	-3	D3	-
Psyk-out grenades	6"	Grenade D3	2	0	1	When resolving an attack made with this weapon against a **PSYKER** or **DAEMON** unit, a hit roll of 6+ inflicts 1 mortal wound on the target and the attack sequence ends.

ABILITIES	Psychic Abomination, Witch Hunters (pg 42)
FACTION KEYWORDS	**IMPERIUM, ASTRA TELEPATHICA, SISTERS OF SILENCE**
KEYWORDS	**INFANTRY, VIGILATORS**

44

WITCHSEEKERS

NAME	M	WS	BS	S	T	W	A	Ld	Sv
Witchseeker	7"	3+	3+	3	3	1	2	8	3+
Sister Superior	7"	3+	3+	3	3	1	3	9	3+

This unit contains 1 Sister Superior and 4 Witchseekers. It can additionally contain up to 5 Witchseekers (**Power Rating +4**). Every model is equipped with: flamer; psyk-out grenades.

WEAPON	RANGE	TYPE	S	AP	D	ABILITIES
Flamer	8"	Assault D6	4	0	1	When resolving an attack made with this weapon, do not make a hit roll: it automatically scores a hit.
Psyk-out grenades	6"	Grenade D3	2	0	1	When resolving an attack made with this weapon against a **PSYKER** or **DAEMON** unit, a hit roll of 6+ inflicts 1 mortal wound on the target and the attack sequence ends.

ABILITIES	Psychic Abomination, Witch Hunters (pg 42)
FACTION KEYWORDS	IMPERIUM, ASTRA TELEPATHICA, SISTERS OF SILENCE
KEYWORDS	INFANTRY, WITCHSEEKERS

NULL-MAIDEN RHINO

DAMAGE
Some of this model's characteristics change as it suffers damage, as shown below:

REMAINING W	M	BS	A
6-10+	12"	3+	3
3-5	6"	4+	D3
1-2	3"	5+	1

NAME	M	WS	BS	S	T	W	A	Ld	Sv
Null-Maiden Rhino	*	6+	*	6	7	10	*	8	3+

A Null-Maiden Rhino is a single model equipped with: storm bolter.

WEAPON	RANGE	TYPE	S	AP	D	ABILITIES
Hunter-killer missile	48"	Heavy 1	8	-2	D6	The bearer can only shoot with each hunter-killer missile it is equipped with once per battle.
Storm bolter	24"	Rapid Fire 2	4	0	1	-

WARGEAR OPTIONS	• This model can additionally be equipped with 1 hunter-killer missile.
ABILITIES	**Explodes:** When this model is destroyed, roll one D6 before any embarked models disembark and before removing it from play. On a 6 it explodes, and each unit within 6" suffers D3 mortal wounds. **Self-Repair:** If this model has lost any wounds, you can roll one D6 at the start of your turn; on a 6 this model regains 1 lost wound. **Smoke Launchers:** Once per battle, instead of shooting in your Shooting phase, this model can use its smoke launchers. Until your next Shooting phase, when resolving an attack made with a ranged weapon against this model, subtract 1 from the hit roll.
TRANSPORT	This model has a transport capacity of 10 SISTERS OF SILENCE INFANTRY models.
FACTION KEYWORDS	IMPERIUM, ASTRA TELEPATHICA, SISTERS OF SILENCE
KEYWORDS	VEHICLE, TRANSPORT, RHINO, NULL-MAIDEN RHINO

SISTERS OF SILENCE STRATAGEMS

If your army is Battle-forged and includes any SISTERS OF SILENCE Detachments (excluding Auxiliary Support Detachments), or any ADEPTUS CUSTODES Detachments that include any SISTERS OF SILENCE units, you can use the Stratagems on this page. These reflect the unique strategies and fighting styles of the Sisters of Silence.

EMPYRIC SEVERANCE
1CP

Sisters of Silence Stratagem

The mere presence of Null-Maidens is enough to quash the psychic manifestations of enemy witches.

Use this Stratagem in your opponent's Psychic phase, when an enemy **PSYKER** manifests a psychic power within 18" of a **SISTERS OF SILENCE INFANTRY** unit from your army, after any Deny the Witch attempt. Roll one D6; on a 3+ that psychic power is resisted and its effects are negated.

TALONS
1CP

Sisters of Silence Stratagem

The Talons of the Emperor strike with deadly unity.

Use this Stratagem in any phase, after shooting or fighting with an **ADEPTUS CUSTODES** unit from your army. Select one friendly **SISTERS OF SILENCE INFANTRY** unit within 6" of that unit. Until the end of that phase, when resolving an attack made by a model in that **SISTERS OF SILENCE** unit, you can re-roll the hit roll.

PUNISHMENT FIRE
1CP

Sisters of Silence Stratagem

Prosecutor squads train to pummel the enemy.

Use this Stratagem in your Shooting phase, when a **PROSECUTORS** unit from your army is chosen to shoot with. Until the end of that phase, change the Range and Type characteristic of boltguns equipped on models in that unit to 18" and Assault 3 respectively.

DESPERATION'S PRICE
1CP

Sisters of Silence Stratagem

To overcome the Null-Maidens' aura, enemy psykers overstretch themselves with horrible consequences.

Use this Stratagem in your opponent's Psychic phase, when an enemy **PSYKER** unit within 18" of a **SISTERS OF SILENCE INFANTRY** unit from your army suffers Perils of the Warp. That **PSYKER** suffers an additional D3 mortal wounds.

CREEPING DREAD
1CP

Sisters of Silence Stratagem

Foes shrink from the Null-Maidens' unsettling presence.

Use this Stratagem at the start of any phase. Select one **SISTERS OF SILENCE INFANTRY** unit from your army. Until the end of that phase, when resolving an attack made by a model in an enemy unit within 6" of that unit, subtract 1 from the hit roll.

DECAPITATING STRIKES
1CP

Sisters of Silence Stratagem

Vigilators train to lop their enemy's heads from their necks, the better to separate witches from their powers.

Use this Stratagem in the Fight phase, when a **VIGILATOR** unit from your army is chosen to fight with. Until the end of that phase, when resolving an attack made with a melee weapon by a model in that unit, add 1 to the wound roll.

PURGATION SWEEP
1/2CP

Sisters of Silence Stratagem

Enough flame can make a pyre of anything.

Use this Stratagem in your Shooting phase. Select a **WITCHSEEKER** unit from your army that contains five or less models for 1CP, or six or more models for 2CP. Until the end of that phase, when determining the number of attacks made by flamer weapons that models in that unit are equipped with, any results of less than 4 count as 4.

IMMATERIAL DISSONANCE
1CP

Sisters of Silence Stratagem

Psyk-out grenades leave their targets reeling.

Use this Stratagem in your Shooting phase or your opponent's Charge phase, after resolving an attack made with a psyk-out grenade by a **SISTERS OF SILENCE** model from your army against a **PSYKER** or **DAEMON** unit that scored a hit. Until the end of that turn, that **PSYKER** or **DAEMON** unit cannot fire Overwatch and when resolving an attack made by a model in that unit, subtract 1 from the hit roll.

SISTERS OF SILENCE NAME GENERATOR

This section is a tool to help you forge names for the Null-Maidens of your Cadre, to further build the background and personality of your army. If you wish to randomly generate a name for one of your Sisters of Silence warriors, you can roll a D66 and consult the table below. To roll a D66, simply roll two D6, one after the other – the first represents tens, and the second represents digits, giving you a result between 11 and 66.

D66	FORENAME	D66	SURNAME
11	Amandera	11	Dakkin
12	Terena	12	Kybus
13	Alyssah	13	Van Loricha
14	Verynech	14	Respus
15	Lyssora	15	Farrondal
16	Eryvane	16	Vydorin
21	Charaleys	21	Lespus
22	Sibella	22	Thrent
23	Phoenica	23	Syrennik
24	Myrella	24	Kyre
25	Charleth	25	Tasmus
26	Siavorna	26	Ghorvash
31	Morgwenna	31	Shayde
32	Zenna	32	Opaline
33	Trinness	33	Maskus
34	Elevor	34	Krenn
35	Argweth	35	Skayde
36	Jalyani	36	Tastrok
41	Kasheyka	41	Klayne
42	Myrelle	42	Masren
43	Verenika	43	Vastys
44	Elyze	44	Vydal
45	Sophea	45	Ultorian
46	Mariatte	46	Weskyn
51	Bethemone	51	Ulmachu
52	Persephyka	52	Nastorus
53	Kariadh	53	Tallobere
54	Rosale	54	Klorica
55	Lorettian	55	Cheynne
56	Channia	56	Dostobreyl
61	Eryka	61	Lengh
62	Brenadh	62	Kendal
63	Maurih	63	Stryke
64	Wynetta	64	Raskus
65	Tasmasin	65	Endrycca
66	Leandra	66	Gaspus

IMPERIAL AGENTS

'There are times when a blade in
the dark, or a single well-aimed
bullet from afar, do more to
topple a world than any number
of tanks, aircraft, witches or
soldiers' guns.'

*- Master Thess, Officio
Assassinorum*

EXECUTION FORCE

The rules in this section can be used in any open play, narrative play or matched play game. They facilitate the inclusion of these lethal paramilitary assets into your Imperial armies, and provide terrifying Stratagems designed to enhance their impact upon the battlefield even further.

This section contains all of the datasheets and Stratagems that you will need in order to fight battles with your Officio Assassinorum models. You will also find rules for including these models in your Imperium armies.

ABILITIES

The following abilities are common to **Officio Assassinorum** units:

Agent of the Imperium

If your army is Battle-forged, you can include 1 **Agent of the Imperium** unit in each **Imperium** (excluding **Fallen**) Patrol, Battalion and Brigade Detachment in your army without those units taking up slots in those Detachments. The inclusion of an **Agent of the Imperium** unit does not prevent other units from their Detachment from benefiting from Detachment abilities (e.g. Chapter Tactics, Defenders of Humanity etc.), and it does not prevent other units from your army benefiting from abilities that require every model in your army to have that ability (e.g. Combat Doctrines). An **Agent of the Imperium** unit included in a Patrol, Battalion or Brigade Detachment in this manner is ignored for any rules that state all units from that Detachment must have at least one Faction keyword in common (e.g. in a matched play game) and when determining your Army Faction.

Execution Force

If your Warlord has the **Imperium** keyword (excluding **Fallen**), you can include this unit in your army as part of a Vanguard Detachment even if that Detachment contains no HQ units. If you do so, that Detachment's Command Benefits are changed to 'None' and its Restrictions are changed to 'This Detachment cannot include the same datasheet more than once.'

Independent Operative

This model can never have a Warlord Trait. During deployment, you can set this model up in concealment instead of placing it on the battlefield. At the end of any of your Movement phases, this model can reveal its position – set it up anywhere on the battlefield that is more than 9" away from any enemy models.

Lightning Reflexes

This model has a 4+ invulnerable save.

POINTS VALUES

If you are playing a matched play game, or a game that uses a points limit, you can use the following to determine the points cost of your army. Simply add together the points costs of all your models to determine your army's total points value.

UNITS

UNIT	MODELS PER UNIT	POINTS PER MODEL (Including wargear)
Callidus Assassin	1	95
Culexus Assassin	1	95
Eversor Assassin	1	95
Vindicare Assassin	1	95

IMPERIAL ASSASSINS

The shadowy agents of the Officio Assassinorum are amongst the most dangerous paramilitary assets available to the Imperium. Specialising in elaborate and arcane forms of murder, each assassin is a living weapon, conditioned to hunt down and slay their target no matter the cost.

Countless enemies of the Imperium have ended their days staring into the ghoulish skull mask of an Imperial assassin, gunned down from afar or pierced by their unseen blades. Be their victim a separatist leader, heretical demagogue, outspoken politico or alien warlord, the assassins will hunt them mercilessly to destruction. No matter what defences their target cowers behind, how big an army they surround themselves with or what unnatural wards and protections they conjure into being, once they have been assigned as a target, their days are numbered and few.

The Officio Assassinorum does not lightly deploy its assets. Every one is a carefully selected specimen, an exemplar of Humanity at the very peak of its mental and physical abilities, further enhanced through augmetic surgery, merciless training regimes and countless hours of hypno-indoctrination. Each Imperial assassin is fashioned into a merciless killing machine, whose only purpose and desire is to eliminate each new target they are assigned with the greatest possible efficiency. In this way do they serve the immortal Emperor of Mankind.

Beneath the shadowy umbrella of the Officio Assassinorum, there are numerous separate temples. Each one teaches its own singular method of murder, substantially different from the next. The Vanus Temple, for instance, engage in assassination through information. Their operatives penetrate the communications hubs and intelligence networks that surround their targets, and employ elaborate remote schemes to ensure their victim's demise. The Venenum Temple, by comparison, are master poisoners. Their agents employ toxins and venoms harvested from myriad sources across the galaxy, tailoring their alchemical murder weapons to their luckless victims to ensure they asphyxiate, haemorrhage, self-immolate or erupt like fleshy volcanoes after the slightest nick of a blade. Yet, perhaps the most broadly effective and universally deadly assassins are those that hail from the Vindicare, Callidus, Eversor and Culexus Temples.

Against the Vindicare Assassin there is no desperate battle for survival, no frantic flight or war of wits. There is only the muffled crack of the assassin's exitus rifle, the violent spray of pulped brain matter, then the graceless tumble of a puppet suddenly shorn of its strings. These lethal marksmen spend days, sometimes months, working their way into the perfect position from which to achieve their killing shot. This is not to say that the Vindicare's only skill is in killing lone targets. Faced by large numbers of battlefield foes, this lethal killer can swiftly rack up a body count that would make a platoon of soldiers proud, snapping off one perfect shot after another until nothing remains but twitching corpses.

The Callidus Assassin is an architect of anarchy, mayhem and misdirection. She uses polymorphine drugs and subdermal implants to shift her shape and fool her foe. The Callidus combines subtle, shadowed killing with expertly sown misinformation to cripple enemy command structures and bring entire battle lines grinding to a halt. Yet, all of this is simply a cover, for first and foremost the Callidus is a killer. Only once the enemy are in utter disarray does the Callidus strike. With a single blast of her neural shredder, this agile assassin reduces the minds of her victims to bubbling soup, while those who fight back are cut to ribbons by the flickering blade of her phase sword.

Between their engineered physique and the combat stimms saturating their system, the Eversor Assassin can run as fast as a speeding skimmer. They can punch a bunker door from its hinges with a single blow, and tear a Chaos Space Marine in two with their bare hands. High Lord Roarch once claimed that the only difference between a cyclonic warhead and an Eversor was that the warhead was kinder, an assertion proved true every time one of these frenzon-fuelled berserkers is deployed. Sent in via drop pod, the Eversor is briefed on their target by subliminal inloads, then set loose to cause utter, bloody mayhem until the victim – and all those around them – are torn to shreds. Even should the Eversor be slain, the foe will not live to enjoy their victory, for the assassin's biochemistry explodes with the force of a plasma bomb.

Most terrifying of all the assassins is the Culexus, before whom panic spreads like a plague. Rendered soulless by their Pariah gene, this assassin projects an aura of absolute fear that can either be masked or amplified by their arcane wargear. One moment the Culexus may be all but invisible, nothing but a flicker of movement in the corner of the enemy's eye, the next they shudders into being, a skull-faced apparition radiating terror as they stalk ever closer. Psykers are racked with unspeakable agony from merely standing in a Culexus' presence, and it is these dangerous individuals the Culexus is sent to slay. Between the soul-searing blasts of their animus speculum and the lethal effects of their psyk-out grenades, no witch can long survive their attentions.

5 POWER

VINDICARE ASSASSIN

NAME	M	WS	BS	S	T	W	A	Ld	Sv
Vindicare Assassin	7"	2+	2+	4	4	5	5	9	6+

A Vindicare Assassin is a single model equipped with: exitus pistol; exitus rifle; blind grenades.

WEAPON	RANGE	TYPE	S	AP	D	ABILITIES
Exitus pistol	12"	Pistol 1	4	-3	D3	When resolving an attack made with this weapon, an invulnerable saving throw cannot be made. Attacks made with this weapon wound **INFANTRY** units on a 2+.
Exitus rifle	72"	Heavy 1	5	-3	D3	When resolving an attack made with this weapon, an invulnerable saving throw cannot be made. Attacks made with this weapon wound **INFANTRY** units on a 2+.
Blind grenades	12"	Grenade D6	*	*	*	This weapon does not inflict any damage (do not make any wound rolls). Instead, if a unit is hit by any blind grenades, subtract 1 from all hit rolls for attacks made by that unit until the end of the turn.

ABILITIES	**Agent of the Imperium, Execution Force, Independent Operative, Lightning Reflexes** (pg 50)	**Head Shot:** If, after resolving an attack with an exitus pistol or exitus rifle by this model, a model in an enemy unit lost any wounds as a result of that attack but was not destroyed, roll one D6; on a 3+ that model suffers 1 mortal wound and, if that model is not destroyed, you can roll one more D6. This time, that model suffers 1 mortal wound on a 4+. Keep rolling one D6, increasing the result required to cause a mortal wound by 1 each time, until the model in the enemy unit being rolled for is destroyed or the roll is failed.
	Deadshot: Attacks made by this model can target a **CHARACTER** unit even if it is not the closest enemy unit. In addition, on an unmodified wound roll of 6 for an attack made with an exitus pistol or exitus rifle, change the Damage characteristic of that weapon to D6 for that attack.	
	Faultless Aim: Attacks made with ranged weapons by this model always hit on a 2+ if this model did not move this turn (hit rolls of 6 are still required when firing Overwatch).	**Spymask:** When resolving an attack made with a ranged weapon by this model, the target does not receive the benefit of cover to its saving throw.
		Stealth Suit: When resolving an attack made with a ranged weapon against this model, subtract 1 from the hit roll. If this model is on or in a terrain feature, subtract 2 from the hit roll instead.

FACTION KEYWORDS	**IMPERIUM, OFFICIO ASSASSINORUM**
KEYWORDS	**INFANTRY, CHARACTER, AGENT OF THE IMPERIUM, VINDICARE ASSASSIN**

CALLIDUS ASSASSIN

NAME	M	WS	BS	S	T	W	A	Ld	Sv
Callidus Assassin	7"	2+	2+	4	4	5	5	9	6+

A Callidus Assassin is a single model equipped with: neural shredder; phase sword; poison blades.

WEAPON	RANGE	TYPE	S	AP	D	ABILITIES
Neural shredder	9"	Assault 1	*	*	*	When resolving an attack with this weapon, if a hit is scored, do not make a wound roll: instead roll 3D6; if the result is equal to or greater than the target unit's highest Leadership characteristic, it suffers D3 mortal wounds.
Phase sword	Melee	Melee	User	-3	2	When resolving an attack made with this weapon, an invulnerable saving throw cannot be made.
Poison blades	Melee	Melee	2	-1	1	When the bearer fights, it makes 1 additional attack with this weapon. Attacks made with this weapon wound on a 3+ unless the target is a **Vehicle** unit.

ABILITIES	**Agent of the Imperium**, **Execution Force**, **Independent Operative**, **Lightning Reflexes** (pg 50)	**Hit and Run:** This model can shoot and charge in a turn in which it Fell Back.
	Polymorphine: During deployment, you can set up this model in disguise instead of setting it up on the battlefield. At the end of any of your Movement phases, this model can revert to its true form – set it up anywhere on the battlefield that is more than D6+3" away from any enemy models. For example, if you roll a 4, the model can be set up anywhere that is more than 7" away from any enemy model.	**Reign of Confusion:** If you have any models with this ability in your army, then in the first battle round, roll one D6 each time your opponent spends Command Points (CPs) to use a Stratagem. On a 4+ your opponent must spend one additional CP to use that Stratagem, or else it has no effect (any CPs spent so far are lost). This ability cannot affect Stratagems used before the battle.
FACTION KEYWORDS	**Imperium, Officio Assassinorum**	
KEYWORDS	**Infantry, Character, Agent of the Imperium, Callidus Assassin**	

EVERSOR ASSASSIN

NAME	M	WS	BS	S	T	W	A	Ld	Sv
Eversor Assassin	7"	2+	2+	4	4	6	6	9	6+

An Eversor Assassin is a single model equipped with: executioner pistol; neuro-gauntlet; power sword; melta bombs.

WEAPON	RANGE	TYPE	S	AP	D	ABILITIES
Executioner pistol	12"	Pistol 4	4	-1	1	You can re-roll wound rolls for attacks made with this weapon that target **Infantry** units.
Neuro-gauntlet	Melee	Melee	+1	-1	1	You can re-roll wound rolls for attacks made with this weapon.
Power sword	Melee	Melee	User	-3	1	-
Melta bombs	4"	Grenade 1	8	-4	D6	You can re-roll wound rolls for attacks made with this weapon that target **Vehicle** units.

ABILITIES	**Agent of the Imperium, Execution Force, Independent Operative, Lightning Reflexes** (pg 50)

Bio-meltdown: If this model is destroyed, before removing the model from the battlefield, roll one D6 for each enemy unit that is within 6" of this model. On a 4+ that enemy unit suffers D3 mortal wounds.

Sentinel Array: Each time an enemy unit Falls Back whilst within 1" of this model, before moving any models, this model can shoot as if it were its Shooting phase. These attacks must target the unit that is Falling Back.

Frenzon: When making a charge roll for this model, roll 3D6 rather than 2D6. In addition, add 2 to this model's Attacks characteristic if it charged or made a Heroic Intervention this turn.

Killing Rampage: Each time a model in an enemy unit is destroyed as the result of an attack made with a melee weapon by this model, you can immediately make one additional attack with a melee weapon this model is equipped with against the same unit. These additional attacks cannot themselves generate further attacks. In addition, this model can consolidate up to 6" instead of up to 3".

FACTION KEYWORDS	**Imperium, Officio Assassinorum**
KEYWORDS	**Infantry, Character, Agent of the Imperium, Eversor Assassin**

CULEXUS ASSASSIN

NAME	M	WS	BS	S	T	W	A	Ld	Sv
Culexus Assassin	7"	2+	2+	4	4	5	4	9	6+

A Culexus Assassin is a single model equipped with: animus speculum; psyk-out grenades.

WEAPON	RANGE	TYPE	S	AP	D	ABILITIES
Animus speculum	18"	Assault D3	5	-4	1	Whilst there are any enemy **Psyker** units within 18" of the bearer, change this weapon's Type characteristic to Assault D6.
Psyk-out grenades	6"	Grenade D3	2	0	1	When resolving an attack made with this weapon against a **Psyker** or **Daemon** unit, a hit roll of 6+ inflicts 1 mortal wound on the target and the attack sequence ends.

ABILITIES	
Agent of the Imperium, **Execution Force**, **Independent Operative**, **Lightning Reflexes** (pg 50) **Abomination:** This model can never be targeted or affected by psychic powers in any way. **Psyker** units that are within 18" of any **Culexus Assassins** must subtract 2 from Psychic tests and Deny the Witch tests they take. **Life Drain:** When resolving an attack made with a melee weapon by this model, a saving throw cannot be made unless it is an invulnerable saving throw.	**Etherium:** When resolving an attack that targets this model, the attacking model is treated as having a Weapon Skill and Ballistic Skill characteristic of 6+. **Psychic Assassin:** Attacks made by this model can target a **Psyker Character** even if it is not the closest enemy unit. In addition, this model can shoot with its psyk-out grenades in the same phase that it shoots with its animus speculum.

FACTION KEYWORDS:	**IMPERIUM, OFFICIO ASSASSINORUM**
KEYWORDS:	**INFANTRY, CHARACTER, AGENT OF THE IMPERIUM, CULEXUS ASSASSIN**

OFFICIO ASSASSINORUM STRATAGEMS

If your army is Battle-forged and includes any IMPERIUM Detachments (that is, a Detachment in which every unit has the IMPERIUM keyword), you have access to the Stratagems shown here, meaning that you can spend Command Points to activate them. These help to reflect the unique tactics used by assassins on the battlefield.

2CP — SHADOW ASSIGNMENT
Officio Assassinorum Stratagem
The enemy have decoded deployment orders for an Assassinorum operative. Yet this 'intelligence' is but another ruse, disguising the true identity of the killer that approaches…

Use this Stratagem before the battle begins. If your army includes exactly 1 OFFICIO ASSASSINORUM unit, remove that unit from your army and then add 1 OFFICIO ASSASSINORUM unit of your choice to your army. The unit that is removed does not count as being destroyed for any rules purposes. Unlike other units that are added to your army, this new unit does not cost any reinforcement points, even in a matched play game.

1CP — TURBO-PENETRATOR ROUND
Vindicare Stratagem
Ripping through the densest armour before detonating, this ammunition is the bane of vehicles and beasts alike.

Use this Stratagem in any phase when a VINDICARE ASSASSIN model from your army makes an attack with an exitus rifle or exitus pistol that targets an opponent's VEHICLE or MONSTER unit. If a hit is scored, the target suffers D3 mortal wounds and the attack sequence ends. If this Stratagem is used then the Head Shot ability does not apply to that attack.

0CP — PRIORITY THREAT NEUTRALISED
Officio Assassinorum Stratagem
Eliminating the enemy's command elements allows a competent commander to seize the strategic initiative.

Use this Stratagem in any phase, when a CHARACTER model in an enemy unit is destroyed by an OFFICIO ASSASSINORUM model from your army. You gain 1 Command Point (or 2 Command Points if the CHARACTER was a Warlord). You can only use this Stratagem once for each enemy CHARACTER model destroyed.

1CP — ACROBATIC
Callidus Stratagem
Callidus Assassins strike with such speed and grace that their targets rarely land a single defensive blow.

Use this Stratagem in your Movement phase. Select one CALLIDUS ASSASSIN model from your army. That model can Advance and charge this turn. In addition, until the start of the next battle round, subtract 1 from hit rolls for attacks that target the selected model.

1CP — PARIAH'S GAZE
Culexus Stratagem
The pure negativity of a Culexus Assassin's soulless presence is focused through their wargear.

Use this Stratagem in your Shooting phase, when you select a CULEXUS ASSASSIN model to shoot with. Until the end of that phase, change the Damage characteristic of that model's animus speculum to D3.

1CP — DOUBLE KILL
Vindicare Stratagem
Vindicare Assassins have been known to fell a second foe before the body of the first has even hit the floor.

Use this Stratagem in your Shooting phase, after a VINDICARE ASSASSIN model from your army shoots. That model can shoot one additional time this phase (this must be at a different target).

SUPREME DECEPTION

2CP

Callidus Stratagem

Operatives of the Callidus Temple are peerless infiltrators, able to disrupt any chain of command.

Use this Stratagem at the start of any battle round after the first. Choose one **CALLIDUS ASSASSIN** from your army (this can be one that is not on the battlefield). That model's Reign of Confusion ability is considered to be in effect until the end of that battle round. You can only use this Stratagem once per battle.

STIMM OVERLOAD

2CP

Eversor Stratagem

Dangerous levels of frenzon flood the Eversor's system, triggering a frenetic killing spree.

Use this Stratagem at the end of the Fight phase. Select one **EVERSOR ASSASSIN** model from your army that fought this phase; that model can fight an additional time this phase. After that model has fought again this phase, roll one D6; on a 1, 2 or 3 it suffers 1 mortal wound.

HYPERMETABOLISM

1CP

Eversor Stratagem

Chemically augmented in the extreme, the bodies of Eversor Assassins can weather injuries that would otherwise prove fatal.

Use this Stratagem at the start of any phase. Select one **EVERSOR ASSASSIN** model from your army. Until the end of that phase, roll one D6 each time that model loses a wound (excluding those lost as the result of a mortal wound); on a 4+ the wound is not lost.

SOUL HORROR

2CP

Culexus Stratagem

An aura of nameless fear surrounds operatives of the Culexus Temple, freezing the hearts of their foes.

Use this Stratagem at the start of the Fight phase. Select one **CULEXUS ASSASSIN** model from your army. Enemy units within 3" of that model cannot be chosen to fight with this phase until after all other units have done so, even if they charged. If one of those units has an ability that allows them to fight first this phase, they instead fight in this phase as if they do not have that ability.

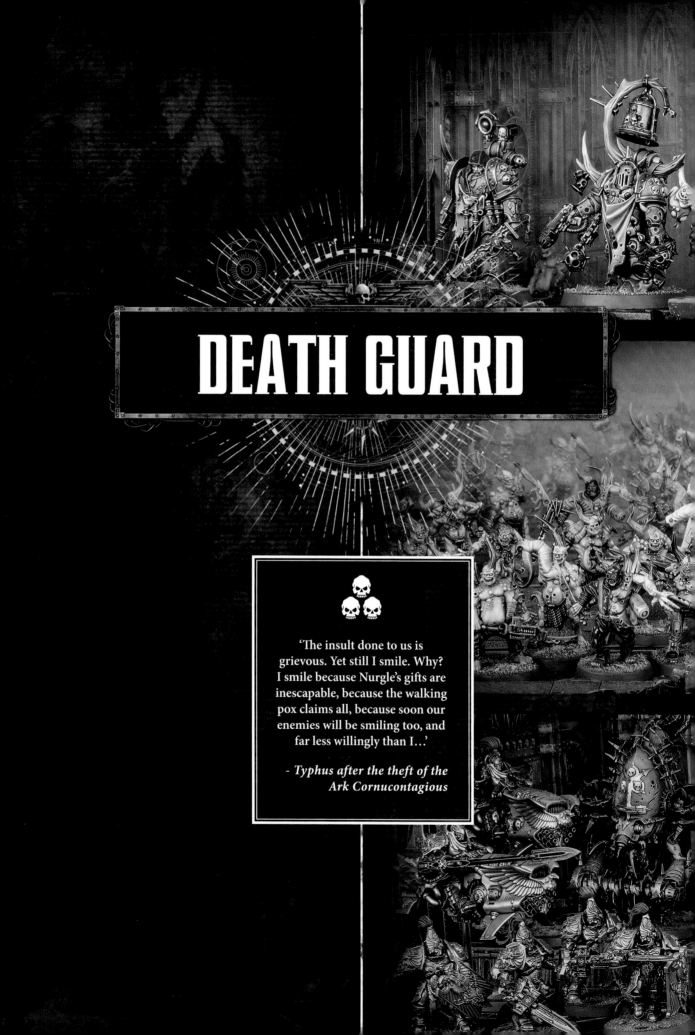

DEATH GUARD

'The insult done to us is grievous. Yet still I smile. Why? I smile because Nurgle's gifts are inescapable, because the walking pox claims all, because soon our enemies will be smiling too, and far less willingly than I…'

- Typhus after the theft of the Ark Cornucontagious

THE FECUND LEGION

In this section you will find new and revised rules for the Death Guard, including army-wide abilities and Stratagems. With Nurgle's blessings, the rules, Stratagems and Relics presented here will aid you in amassing your revolting plague-worshippers into a vectorium fit to rot the very stars from the withering heavens.

This section is a supplement to *Codex: Death Guard* – you will need a copy of that book to use the rules in this section.

This section contains Relics, Warlord Traits and Stratagems that allow you to field a force representing each of the Plague Companies of the Death Guard. You will also find additional Relics and Stratagems that can be used with any Death Guard army, and a name generator with which you can personalise your characters.

ABILITIES

All **DEATH GUARD** units from *Codex: Death Guard* without the **CHAOS CULTISTS** or **POXWALKERS** keywords gain the Hateful Assault and Malicious Volleys abilities, below.

HATEFUL ASSAULT

If this unit makes a charge move, is charged or performs a Heroic Intervention, add 1 to the Attacks characteristic of models in this unit until the end of the turn.

MALICIOUS VOLLEYS

Instead of following the normal rules for Rapid Fire weapons, models in this unit firing Rapid Fire bolt weapons make double the number of attacks if any of the following apply:

- The firing model's target is within half the weapon's maximum range.

- The firing model is **INFANTRY** and every model in its unit Remained Stationary in your previous Movement phase.

- The firing model is a **TERMINATOR** or **HELBRUTE**.

For the purposes of this ability, a Rapid Fire bolt weapon is any bolt weapon with the Rapid Fire type.

BOLT WEAPONS

A bolt weapon is any weapon whose profile includes the word 'bolt' (boltgun, bolt pistol, etc.), and any Relic that replaces a bolt weapon.

Rules that apply to bolt weapons also apply to the boltgun profile of combi-weapons (see *Codex: Death Guard*), and the bolter profile of Relics that replace combi-weapons.

PLAGUE WEAPONS

A plague weapon is any weapon whose profile includes the word 'plague' (plague knife, plaguesword, etc.), any weapon with the Plague Weapon ability (see *Codex: Death Guard*), and any Relic that replaces a plague weapon.

RELICS OF DECAY

It is said of Nurgle that he is a generous deity. Certainly, those champions who claim to work the Plague God's will bear a strange and horrible array of disease-ridden gifts, be they pox-seeping weapons of war, rust-caked slabs of warp-ensorcelled armour or weird arcana that seethe with the powers of plague.

If your army is led by a **DEATH GUARD** Warlord, you can give one of the following Relics of Decay to a **DEATH GUARD CHARACTER** model from your army instead of giving them a Relic from *Codex: Death Guard*. Named characters (such as **TYPHUS**) cannot be given the following Relics.

Note that some Relics are weapons that replace one of the model's existing weapons. Where this is the case, you must, if you are using points values, still pay the cost of the weapon that is being replaced. Write down any Relics your models have on your army roster.

THE AGUE STONE

This curse-iron pendant radiates contagious energies that cause the enemy to shake with feverish weakness.

LORD OF CONTAGION model only. Subtract 1 from the Strength characteristic of enemy models whilst their unit is within 3" of a model from your army with this Relic.

ALLWYTHER

The presence of this unholy blade causes reality itself to fade, shrivel and rot away. No armour, warding, arcane technology or witch's hex can stay its baleful touch.

Model equipped with a balesword only. This Relic replaces a balesword and has the following profile:

WEAPON	RANGE	TYPE	S	AP	D
Allwyther	Melee	Melee	+1	-3	2

Abilities: Plague Weapon (see *Codex: Death Guard*). When resolving an attack made with this weapon, an invulnerable saving throw cannot be made.

THE DAEMON'S TOLL

With each discordant note, this warp-forged bell sends Mortarion's sons shuddering out of sync with realspace. They quiver upon the cusp of the empyrean, allowing its unholy energies to flow forth and enfold them.

NOXIOUS BLIGHTBRINGER model only. Models in friendly **DEATH GUARD** units (excluding **CHAOS CULTISTS** and **POXWALKERS** units) have a 5+ invulnerable save whilst their unit is within 7" of a model from your army with this Relic.

THE EPIDEMICYST BLADE

This revolting weapon squirms with fattened buboes that burst and spatter their filth across the foe with every blow. Its juices burn and corrupt, seeping through chinks in the enemy's armour and eating away at their flesh.

Model equipped with a hellforged sword only. This Relic replaces a hellforged sword and has the following profile:

WEAPON	RANGE	TYPE	S	AP	D
The Epidemicyst Blade	Melee	Melee	+1	-2	3

Abilities: Plague Weapon (see *Codex: Death Guard*). When resolving an attack made with this weapon, an unmodified hit roll of 6 scores 1 additional hit.

THE PUTRID PERIAPT

Plucked from the gut of one of Horticulous Slimux's own Beasts of Nurgle, this revolting amulet reacts to dark witchery by releasing clouds of warp-spores that seed the flesh of Nurgle's faithful with fecund vitality.

PSYKER model only. A model with this Relic knows one additional psychic power. Once in each of your Psychic phases, after a psychic power is resolved that was manifested by a model with this Relic, that model can regain up to D3 lost wounds.

WORMSPITTER

This bloated bolt pistol fires shells that burst in showers of Daemon maggots. These squirm everywhere with squeals of glee, gnawing, vomiting and defaecating until their victims are crawling with corrosive rustpox.

Model equipped with a bolt pistol only. This Relic replaces a bolt pistol and has the following profile:

WEAPON	RANGE	TYPE	S	AP	D
Wormspitter	15"	Pistol 1	5	-2	1

Abilities: Plague Weapon (see *Codex: Death Guard*). When resolving an attack made with this weapon, if a hit is scored, the target is corroded until the end of the turn. When resolving an attack made with a weapon by a friendly **DEATH GUARD** model against a corroded unit, that weapon gains the Plague Weapon ability for that attack.

DEATH GUARD STRATAGEMS

If your army is Battle-forged and includes any DEATH GUARD Detachments (excluding Auxiliary Support Detachments), you have access to the Stratagems shown here, and can spend Command Points to activate them. These reflect the unique strategies used by the forces of the Death Guard on the battlefield.

PLAGUECHOSEN
1CP

Death Guard Stratagem

Many heroes of the Death Guard have favoured lieutenants who fight amidst their ranks.

Use this Stratagem before the battle, after nominating your Warlord. Select one DEATH GUARD CHARACTER model from your army that does not have a Warlord Trait and determine one Warlord Trait for it; it is regarded as your Warlord for the purposes of that Warlord Trait. Each Warlord Trait in your army must be unique (if randomly generated, re-roll duplicate results).

SOUL HARVEST
1CP

Death Guard Stratagem

The Daemon Prince swings its blade in scything arcs that harvest the enemies' souls from their bodies.

Use this Stratagem in the Fight phase when a DEATH GUARD DAEMON PRINCE model from your army that is equipped with a daemonic axe or hellforged sword is chosen to fight with. Until the end of that phase, add 3 to that model's Attacks characteristic, and only INFANTRY units can be chosen as the target of its attacks.

HARBINGER OF NURGLE
1CP

Death Guard Stratagem

Those Death Guard lords believed to be marked by the Plague God inspire contagious vigour in their warriors.

Use this Stratagem before the battle. Select one LORD OF CONTAGION unit from your army. Until the end of the battle, that unit has the following ability:

'Harbinger of Nurgle: Re-roll hit rolls of 1 for attacks made by models in friendly DEATH GUARD units whilst their unit is within 6" of this model.'

FOULGUSH
1CP

Death Guard Stratagem

The Blightspawn strains at the seams with churning slime before spewing it forth in a peristaltic gush.

Use this Stratagem in your Shooting phase when a FOUL BLIGHTSPAWN model from your army is chosen to shoot with. Until the end of that phase, when rolling to determine the number of attacks made with a plague sprayer by that model, roll one additional D6 and discard one of the dice. In addition, until the end of that phase, when rolling to determine the Strength characteristic of that weapon, roll one additional D6 and discard one of the dice.

VIRULENT ROUNDS
1CP

Death Guard Stratagem

The Death Guard know countless revolting ways to render their bolt rounds lethally virulent.

Use this Stratagem in your Shooting phase when a PLAGUE MARINES unit from your army is chosen to shoot with. Until the end of that phase, bolt weapons models in that unit are equipped with gain the following abilities:

'Plague Weapon (see *Codex: Death Guard*). When resolving an attack made with this weapon against an INFANTRY unit, on an unmodified wound roll of 6 the Armour Penetration characteristic of this weapon is -4 for that attack. '

RELENTLESS VOLLEYS
1/2CP

Death Guard Stratagem

Always have the Death Guard had a reputation as masters of the merciless close-range firefight.

Use this Stratagem in your Shooting phase when a DEATH GUARD INFANTRY unit from your army is chosen to shoot with. Until the end of that phase, boltguns and the boltgun profile of combi-weapons (see *Codex: Death Guard*) models in that unit are equipped with have a Type characteristic of Rapid Fire 2. In addition, until the end of that phase, combi-bolters models in that unit are equipped with have a Type characteristic of Rapid Fire 3. If that unit contains 6 or more models, this Stratagem costs 2CP.

PUTRID FECUNDITY
2/3CP

Death Guard Stratagem

These bloated warriors' wounds are staunched with rancid flesh as fast as the foe can inflict them.

Use this Stratagem in your opponent's Shooting phase or the Fight phase when a **Plague Marines** unit from your army is chosen as the target for an attack. If that unit contains 10 or fewer models then this Stratagem costs 2 Command Points; otherwise it costs 3 Command Points. Until the end of that phase, when making a Disgustingly Resilient roll (see *Codex: Death Guard*) for a model in that unit, add 1 to that roll.

HYPERTOXIC TINCTURES
1CP

Death Guard Stratagem

This foul plague-alchemist anoints his comrades' weapons with his latest batches of infectious toxins.

Use this Stratagem before the battle. Select one **Plague Surgeon** model from your army. Until the end of the battle, that model has the following ability:

'**Hypertoxic Tinctures:** Re-roll wound rolls of 1 or 2 for attacks made with plague weapons by models in friendly **Death Guard** units whilst their unit is within 6" of this model.'

TRENCH-FIGHTERS
1CP

Death Guard Stratagem

The Death Guard excel in the crush of close quarters, driving plague knives into their victims again and again.

Use this Stratagem in the Fight phase when a **Plague Marines** unit from your army is chosen to fight with. Until the end of that phase, when a model in that unit fights, if it is equipped with one or more plague knives, it can make one additional attack with one plague knife.

NOXIOUS RUPTURE
1CP

Death Guard Stratagem

Even in death, those blessed by Nurgle splatter, spurt and spew their god's foul gifts far and wide.

Use this Stratagem in any phase other than the Morale phase when the last model in a **Death Guard** unit from your army is destroyed, before removing that model from play. Select one enemy unit within 3" of that model. Until the end of your opponent's next turn, when resolving an attack made by a model from the selected unit, subtract 1 from the hit roll.

CREEPING BLIGHT
1CP

Death Guard Stratagem

This warp-plague spreads fingers of corrosion through armour, flesh, bone and even air with equal virulence.

Use this Stratagem in the Fight phase when a **Death Guard** unit from your army is chosen to fight with. Until the end of that phase, when resolving an attack made with a weapon by a model in that unit, add 1 to any damage roll made for that attack, and on an unmodified wound roll of 6 the Armour Penetration characteristic of that weapon is -4 for that attack.

ERUPTION OF FILTH
1CP

Death Guard Stratagem

The slain warrior bursts like a fat, pox-laden bubo.

Use this Stratagem when a **Death Guard Terminator** model from your army is destroyed, before removing that model from play. Roll one D6 for each unit within 7" that does not have the **Nurgle** keyword. On a 4+ the unit being rolled for suffers 1 mortal wound.

MUTANT STRAIN
1CP

Death Guard Stratagem

Unholy diseases warp and mutate, sending their carriers into a froth-jawed killing fever to the ruin of all.

Use this Stratagem in the Fight phase when a **Poxwalkers** unit from your army is chosen to fight with. Until the end of that phase, when resolving an attack made with a melee weapon by a model in that unit against an **Infantry** unit, an unmodified wound roll of 6 inflicts 1 mortal wound on the target and the attack sequence ends, and on an unmodified hit roll of 1, that model's unit suffers 1 mortal wound.

WARP TOLL
1CP

Death Guard Stratagem

Empyric energies imbue the tocsin's tolling with dread.

Use this Stratagem at the start of the Morale phase. Select one **Noxious Blightbringer** model from your army. Until the end of that phase, when taking a Morale test for an enemy unit within 7" of that model, add 1 to the roll. In addition, if that Morale test is failed, double the number of models that flee.

MIASMAL AFFLICTIONS

2CP

Death Guard Stratagem

Toxic clouds of unclean fumes and spores billow from every pipe and rent in the Plague Marines' foul armour.

Use this Stratagem at the start of the Fight phase. Select one enemy unit within 1" of a **PLAGUE MARINES** unit from your army. Until the end of that phase, subtract 1 from the Toughness characteristic of models in that enemy unit whilst it is not within range of **MORTARION**'s Toxic Presence ability.

LIFE-EATER

1CP

Death Guard Stratagem

A strain of the daemonic life-eater phage infests these warriors' blades, aggressively reducing all it touches to drizzling filth and bubbling sludge.

Use this Stratagem in the Fight phase when a **DEATH GUARD** unit from your army is chosen to fight with. Until the end of that phase, when resolving an attack made with a plague weapon by a model in that unit, an unmodified hit roll of 6 automatically scores a hit and successfully wounds the target (do not make a wound roll).

OVERWHELMING GENEROSITY

1CP

Death Guard Stratagem

Unholy filth gushes from Nurgle's faithful into their guns until the armaments threaten to burst like bloated corpses.

Use this Stratagem in your Shooting phase when a **DEATH GUARD** unit from your army (excluding **CHAOS CULTISTS** or **POXWALKERS** units) is chosen to shoot with. Until the end of that phase, add 6" to the range of Plague Weapons (see *Codex: Death Guard*), excluding melee weapons, models in that unit are equipped with.

ACCELERATED ENTROPY

1CP

Death Guard Stratagem

Enhanced with runic rot-stones from the Plague Planet itself, these cannons are rendered more lethal than ever.

Use this Stratagem before the battle. Select one **PLAGUEBURST CRAWLER** model from your army. Until the end of the battle, entropy cannons that model, and all friendly **PLAGUEBURST CRAWLER** models within 7" of that model, are equipped with have the following abilities:

'Plague Weapon (see *Codex: Death Guard*). When resolving an attack made with this weapon, a damage roll of 1 or 2 counts as 3 instead.'

FIRE FEVER

1CP

Death Guard Stratagem

Empyric fever-heat burns through the Helbrute's brain, causing it to fire with ever more frenzied ferocity.

Use this Stratagem in your Shooting phase after you have declared how you will split the shots of a **HELBRUTE** model from your army that is equipped with two ranged weapons. Until the end of that phase, if that model shoots all of its weapons at the same target, when resolving an attack made by that model, you can re-roll the hit roll.

CONTAMINATED MONSTROSITY

1CP

Death Guard Stratagem

Whether a seething flesh-hulk or blighted war engine, this foul horror pulsates with unclean fecundity.

Use this Stratagem before the battle. Select one **DEATH GUARD** unit (excluding **CHAOS CULTISTS** and **TITANIC** units) from your army with a Wounds characteristic of 12 or less for 1CP, or 13 or more for 2CP. Until the end of the battle, if that unit does not have the Disgustingly Resilient ability (see *Codex: Death Guard*), it gains the Disgustingly Resilient ability.

PARASITIC FUMES

1CP

Death Guard Stratagem

Gnawing, microbial Daemon-parasites swarm amidst the fumes that spill from the Blighthaulers' exhausts.

Use this Stratagem at the end of your Movement phase. Select one **MYPHITIC BLIGHT-HAULERS** unit from your army. Until the end of the turn, when an attack is allocated to an enemy model within 7" of that unit, improve the Armour Penetration characteristic of the weapon that attack is being made with by 1 for that attack (e.g. AP 0 becomes AP -1).

PLAGUE COMPANIES

Unusually for the Traitor Legions, Mortarion's Death Guard have retained much of their old cohesion and built upon it, their numbers proliferating like unholy bacteria within the Eye of Terror. Vectorium warbands from the seven Plague Companies bedevil the galaxy, each fighting in their own repugnant fashion.

If your army is Battle-forged and includes any **DEATH GUARD** Detachments, you can select which Plague Company each of those Detachments belongs to from the seven listed on the following pages. If you do, all **DEATH GUARD** units from that Detachment (excluding **CHAOS CULTISTS** and **POXWALKERS** units, and named characters such as **TYPHUS**) gain the relevant **<PLAGUE COMPANY>** Faction keyword.

For example, if your army includes a **DEATH GUARD** Detachment containing a **LORD OF CONTAGION** unit, two units of **PLAGUE MARINES** and a unit of **POXWALKERS**, and you decide that Detachment is from the Ferrymen, all those units, except the **POXWALKERS**, would gain the **FERRYMEN** Faction keyword.

A **DEATH GUARD** Detachment that belongs to one of the seven Plague Companies has access to the rules described below.

WARLORD TRAITS

If a **DEATH GUARD <PLAGUE COMPANY> CHARACTER** model is your Warlord, they can have the relevant **<PLAGUE COMPANY>** Warlord Trait instead of a Warlord Trait from *Codex: Death Guard*.

PUTRESCENT RELICS

If your army is led by a **DEATH GUARD <PLAGUE COMPANY>** Warlord, you can give the relevant **<PLAGUE COMPANY>** Putrescent Relic to a **DEATH GUARD <PLAGUE COMPANY> CHARACTER** model from your army instead of giving them a Relic of Decay from *Codex: Death Guard* or elsewhere in this publication. Named characters (such as **TYPHUS**) cannot be given a Putrescent Relic.

Note that some Relics are weapons that replace one of the model's existing weapons. Where this is the case, you must, if you are using points values, still pay the cost of the weapon that is being replaced. Write down any Relics your models have on your army roster.

STRATAGEMS

You have access to the relevant **<PLAGUE COMPANY>** Stratagems, and can spend Command Points to activate them.

THE HARBINGERS

The 1st Plague Company is ruled over by Typhus the Traveller, and its forces are often called the Harbingers. This Plague Company's ranks are infested with hundreds of strains of the zombie plague, including Shamblerot, the Groaning and Biter's Pox.

If this Detachment contains Typhus, that model gains the **HARBINGERS** Faction keyword.

If this Detachment contains any **POXWALKERS** units, those units gain the **HARBINGERS** Faction keyword.

WARLORD TRAIT: SHAMBLEROT

With every blow this warlord spreads the dreaded Shamblerot, fallen enemies rising again like half-strung puppets with green fire burning in their eyes.

When an enemy **INFANTRY** model is destroyed as the result of an attack made with a melee weapon by this Warlord, add one model to a friendly **HARBINGERS POXWALKERS** unit within 7" of this Warlord. You must pay reinforcement points for each model that you add to that unit that would increase that unit above its starting strength.

PUTRESCENT RELIC: ROTSKULL BOMB

This balloon-like grenade contains gallons of virulent slop, crammed through sorcerous means into a bloated Poxwalker skull whose fixed grin constantly drizzles slime.

Model equipped with a blight grenade only. This Relic replaces a blight grenade and has the following profile:

WEAPON	RANGE	TYPE	S	AP	D
Rotskull Bomb	6"	Grenade 2D3	5	-2	2

Abilities: Plague Weapon (see *Codex: Death Guard*). When resolving an attack made with this weapon, do not make a hit roll: it automatically scores a hit.

1/3CP

FROM THE CARRION HEAPS
Harbingers Stratagem
One should always burn the bodies of the plague-slain, lest they rise again to assail those still living.

Use this Stratagem before the battle. Select one **HARBINGERS POXWALKERS** unit from your army for 1 Command Point, or two **HARBINGERS POXWALKERS** units from your army for 3 Command Points. You can set up the selected units under the ground instead of setting them up on the battlefield. At the end of your Movement phase, for each of the units that are under the ground, you can set up that unit anywhere on the battlefield that is wholly within 9" of a battlefield edge and more than 9" away from any enemy models. You can only use this Stratagem once per battle.

1CP

LIFE BEYOND DEATH
Harbingers Stratagem
The plagues infesting this warrior keep them clawing and biting for several moments even after their demise.

Use this Stratagem in the Fight Phase when the last model in a **HARBINGERS** unit from your army is destroyed as the result of an attack. The unit containing the model that made that attack suffers D3 mortal wounds.

THE INEXORABLE

The 2nd Plague Company favours mechanised assaults. Known as the Inexorable for the crushing nature of its advance, it boasts huge formations of lumbering battle tanks. Its warriors bear the Ferric Blight, which speckles their armour and vehicles with crawling rust that can swiftly infest the foe.

WARLORD TRAIT: FERRIC BLIGHT

The creeping plague-rust that makes this warlord's every movement creak and grate also lends his attacks the ability to rapidly infest the foe's war engines.

When resolving an attack made with a weapon by a friendly **INEXORABLE** model against an enemy **VEHICLE** unit within 7" of this Warlord, improve the Armour Penetration characteristic of that weapon by 1 for that attack (e.g. AP 0 becomes AP -1).

PUTRESCENT RELIC: THE LEECHSPORE CASKET

This armoured, rune-inscribed chest is borne to battle aboard the war engines of the Inexorable. Through unclean sorcery it is bound to the soul of a mighty plague champion; as that warrior reaps a tally amongst the foe, so the casket creaks open and spews fecund spores that use the enemy's parasitised life force to heal the vehicle's hurts with putrid mutant flesh.

When a model is destroyed as a result of an attack made with a melee weapon by a model from your army with this Relic, one friendly **INEXORABLE VEHICLE** model within 18" regains up to one lost wound. Each model from your army can regain up to three lost wounds per turn as a result of this ability.

1CP — UNHOLY ESSENCE
Inexorable Stratagem

The tanks of the Inexorable squirm with unnatural vitality and diseased vigour.

Use this Stratagem at the start of your Shooting phase. Select up to three **INEXORABLE VEHICLE** units from your army. Until the end of that phase, those units gain the Inexorable Advance ability (see *Codex: Death Guard*).

1CP — FERRIC MIASMA
Inexorable Stratagem

As the foe press forward they are engulfed in a whirling storm of flesh-rust flakes that clog lungs and eyes.

Use this Stratagem in your opponent's Charge phase when a **INEXORABLE** unit from your army is chosen as a target of a charge declared for an **INFANTRY** unit. Subtract 2 from the charge roll made for that charge.

MORTARION'S ANVIL

Known as Mortarion's Anvil, the warriors of the 3rd Plague Company excel at digging in and letting their foes dash themselves apart against their defences. They carry the Gloaming Bloat, a plague of fever sweats that slicks their armour and causes them to speak in wet gurgles.

WARLORD TRAIT: GLOAMING BLOAT

Striking at this warlord is like piercing a drowned corpse; fluids and tattered flesh might spill forth in foetid clouds, but to do any real harm is tremendously difficult.

When resolving an attack made against this Warlord, an unmodified wound roll of 1-3 always fails, irrespective of any abilities that the weapon or the model making that attack has.

PUTRESCENT RELIC: TOLLKEEPER

This macabre device of rotwood, rust and bone was fashioned by the Great Unclean One Pedangrulox to help him tally the blights and plagues he unleashed. So saturated with those same plagues did the foul artefact become that now the mere act of tallying the slain with it causes unclean outbreaks to erupt amongst their comrades.

TALLYMAN model only. When resolving an attack made with a melee weapon by a model in a **MORTARION'S ANVIL** unit from your army within 7" of a friendly model with this Relic, an unmodified hit roll of 6 scores one additional hit.

2/3CP — FUTILITY MADE FLESH
Mortarion's Anvil Stratagem
No matter how much fire the foe pours into these indomitable warriors, it is never enough…

Use this Stratagem in your opponent's Shooting phase when a **MORTARION'S ANVIL TERMINATOR** unit from your army is chosen as the target for an attack. Until the end of that phase, when resolving an attack made with a weapon against that unit, reduce the Damage characteristic of that weapon by 1, to a minimum of 1, for that attack. If that unit contains 5 or fewer models, this Stratagem costs 2CP; otherwise, it costs 3CP.

1CP — RELAPTIC ASSAULT
Mortarion's Anvil Stratagem
Like a sickness flaring back to life, these stolid warriors erupt from their dug-in positions to counter-attack.

Use this Stratagem in your opponent's Charge phase. Select one **MORTARION'S ANVIL INFANTRY** unit from your army. Until the end of that phase, that unit can perform a Heroic Intervention as if it were a **CHARACTER**.

THE WRETCHED

The 4th Plague Company is ruled over by the gestalt Daemon known as the Eater of Lives. Its Legionnaires carry the Eater Plague, also called drizzleflesh, pockchewer and the endless gift. The Company is known as the Wretched, for its inhuman master favours Sorcerers and summonation in defiance of Mortarion's virtual taboo against such things.

WARLORD TRAIT: EATER PLAGUE

The flesh melting horror of the Eater Plague pours off this warlord in waves, reducing his foes to bubbling gruel that he daubs into his own wounds by the fistful to plug them.

When an enemy model is destroyed as the result of an attack made with a melee weapon by this Warlord, this Warlord regains up to one lost wound (to a maximum of 3 wounds per phase).

PUTRESCENT RELIC: THE DAEMON'S FAVOUR

This vile, crater-pocked poppet-doll is scrimshawed from diseased bone. It teems with the malevolent essence of the Eater of Lives himself, his power billowing forth in gnawing clouds to dissolve its bearer's foes.

MALIGNANT PLAGUECASTER model only. A model from your army with this Relic replaces its Pestilential Fallout ability with the following:

'**Torrent of Putrefaction**: After resolving a psychic power manifested by this model, if the result of the Psychic test for that power was less than 7, the nearest enemy unit within 7" of this model suffers 1 mortal wound. In addition, if the result of the Psychic test for that power was 7 or more, select one enemy unit within 7" of this model. That unit suffers D3 mortal wounds.'

1CP — THE ROTTED VEIL
Wretched Stratagem
The mere presence of this chanting, shambling champion causes the barriers of reality to wither and weaken.

Use this Stratagem at the end of your Movement phase. Select one **WRETCHED CHARACTER** unit from your army that has not performed a Daemonic Ritual this turn. That unit can perform a Daemonic Ritual (see *Codex: Death Guard*) as if it were your Movement phase and that model had not moved, regardless of whether or not it arrived as reinforcements this turn. In addition, until the end of the turn, when that unit performs a Daemonic Ritual, only roll one D6 for the summoning roll, and add 7 to the result.

1CP — SEVENFOLD BLESSINGS
Wretched Stratagem
This diseased sorcerer feels the rheumy eye of the Plague God upon him.

Use this Stratagem before the battle. Select one **WRETCHED PSYKER** model from your army. Until the end of the battle, when a Psychic test is taken for that model, you can re-roll one of the dice. You can only use this Stratagem once per battle.

THE POXMONGERS

Known to many as the Poxmongers, the 5th Plague Company makes great use of diseased Daemon Engines when it goes into battle. Its forces carry the Sanguous Flux, which causes endless, half-clotted bleeding and leaves foul red-black trails behind them wherever they go.

WARLORD TRAIT: SANGUOUS FLUX

Foes near to this warlord feel their flesh and armour alike splitting open in wet, red rents and weals, through which the Poxmongers can more easily plunge their diseased blades.

When resolving an attack made with a melee weapon by a friendly **POXMONGERS** model against an enemy **INFANTRY** unit whilst that model's unit is within 7" of this Warlord, improve the Armour Penetration characteristic of that weapon by 1 for that attack (e.g. AP 0 becomes AP -1).

PUTRESCENT RELIC: IRONCLOT FURNACE

Comprising an ever-burning alchemical engine lodged within the bearer's armour and an array of rune-carved, coiling tubes and exhausts that spill from it, this foul artefact churns out warp-charged pollutants that coat nearby Daemon Engines.

Models in **POXMONGERS DAEMON ENGINE** units from your army have a 4+ invulnerable save whilst their unit is within 7" of a friendly model with this Relic.

1CP

BILIOUS BLOODRUSH
Poxmongers Stratagem
The diseased gore flowing through and across this Daemon Engine boils and bubbles as its rage burns hot.

Use this Stratagem in your Shooting phase. Select one **POXMONGERS DAEMON ENGINE** unit from your army. Until the end of that phase, that unit can shoot in a turn in which it Fell Back.

1CP

THE FLUX ABATED
Poxmongers Stratagem
Worrying greedily at its victim, the Daemon Engine devours puissance to heal its ever bleeding hide.

Use this Stratagem in the Fight phase when an enemy model is destroyed as the result of an attack made by a model in a **POXMONGERS DAEMON ENGINE** unit from your army. One model in that unit can regain up to D3 lost wounds.

THE FERRYMEN

Called the Ferrymen or the Brethren of the Fly, the 6th Plague Company garrisons the Plague Fleets, and acquires new ships for their suppurating armadas. It boasts large numbers of Blightlord Terminators riddled with the parasite known as the Droning.

WARLORD TRAIT: THE DRONING

A blizzard of fist-sized daemonic flies whirls around this warlord, biting, stinging and scrabbling madly to drive his enemies back in terrified revulsion.

When a Morale test is taken for an enemy unit within 12" of this Warlord, add 2 to the result.

PUTRESCENT RELIC: THE FERRYMAN'S SCYTHE

This grotesquely oversized weapon lops great chunks of armour and flesh from its victims, each lumpen gobbet taken as payment for ferrying the victim's soul through the veil and into Nurgle's malignant garden for all eternity.

Model equipped with a plaguereaper only. This Relic replaces a plaguereaper and has the following profile:

WEAPON	RANGE	TYPE	S	AP	D
The Ferryman's Scythe	Melee	Melee	+4	-3	3

Abilities: Plague Weapon (see *Codex: Death Guard*). When resolving an attack made with this weapon, an unmodified wound roll of 6 inflicts 1 mortal wound on the target in addition to any other damage.

1CP

VERMID WHISPERS
Ferrymen Stratagem
The compound eyes and keening whispers of countless daemonic flies help guide these warriors' aim.

Use this Stratagem in your Shooting phase when a **FERRYMEN BLIGHTLORD TERMINATORS** unit from your army is chosen to shoot with. Until the end of that phase, when resolving an attack made by a model in that unit, add 1 to the hit roll.

2CP

ON DRONING WINGS
Ferrymen Stratagem
Buzzing clouds of plague flies billow from these warriors, acting as vectors for their unholy gifts.

Use this Stratagem at the start of the Movement phase. Select one **FERRYMEN** unit from your army. Until the end of the turn, the range of that unit's aura abilities is increased by 7" (note that the Nurgle's Gift ability still only affects enemy units within 1" of an affected friendly unit).

MORTARION'S CHOSEN SONS

Those of the 7th Plague Company have the honour of being the Daemon Primarch Mortarion's Chosen Sons. They are plague brewers and dark alchemists, and are blessed by Nurgle with the Crawling Pustulance, also known as boilblight, lumpen splatter and Nurgle's fruit.

WARLORD TRAIT: CRAWLING PUSTULANCE

This warlord's flesh is thickly layered with pustules that absorb the fury of his foe's attacks, and which burst and spatter corrosive fluids across those who try to flee him.

When resolving an attack made with a melee weapon against this Warlord, subtract 1 from the hit roll. When an enemy unit (excluding units that can **FLY**) within 1" of this Warlord Falls Back, roll one D6; on a 2+ that unit suffers D3 mortal wounds.

PUTRESCENT RELIC: VOMITRYX

This gruesome weapon contains a microscopic warp portal that leads directly into the festering guts of the Great Unclean One Ku'Gath. When its nozzle is opened it spews ferocious gouts of the Daemon's highly corrosive bile.

Model equipped with a plague sprayer only. This Relic replaces a plague sprayer and has the following profile:

WEAPON	RANGE	TYPE	S	AP	D
Vomitryx	9"	Assault 7	7	-3	2

Abilities: Plague Weapon (see *Codex: Death Guard*). When resolving an attack made with this weapon, do not make a hit roll: it automatically scores a hit.

1CP — ALEMBICHAL NARTHECIUM
Mortarion's Chosen Sons Stratagem
Gifted to his sons by Mortarion himself, this arcane device invigorates their unclean physiognomies.

Use this Stratagem before the battle. Select one **MORTARION'S CHOSEN SONS PLAGUE SURGEON** model from your army. Until the end of the battle, replace that model's Tainted Narthecium ability with the following:

'**Alembichal Narthecium:** When making a Disgustingly Resilient roll for a friendly **MORTARION'S CHOSEN SONS INFANTRY** model whilst its unit is within 3" of this model, you can re-roll a roll of 1 or 2.'

1CP — PLAGUE BREWERS
Mortarion's Chosen Sons Stratagem
No Plague Company boasts a more gruesome array of potions, poisons and unclean fluids than the 7th.

Use this Stratagem in your Shooting phase when a **MORTARION'S CHOSEN SONS** unit from your army is chosen to shoot with. Until the end of that phase, plague belchers, plaguespurt gauntlets and plague spewers that models in that unit are equipped with have a Damage characteristic of 2.

DEATH GUARD NAME GENERATOR

This section will help you to assign suitably revolting names to your diseased champions of Nurgle, to further build the background and personality of your army. If you wish to randomly generate a name for one of your Death Guard warriors, you can roll a D66 and consult one or both of the tables below. To roll a D66, simply roll two D6, one after the other – the first represents tens, and the second represents digits, giving you a result between 11 and 66.

D66	FORENAME	D66	SURNAME
11	Excresmus	11	Gloagh
12	Mulghus	12	Grulgh
13	Phleggan	13	Drohne
14	One-Horn	14	Spute
15	Thrulgh	15	Gnurr
16	Oghlos	16	Foultouch
21	Hweaghun	21	the Ruptured
22	Sloppoth	22	Sepk
23	Vulgor	23	the Unclean
24	Quismus	24	Foulgoit
25	Anphlax	25	the Rancid
26	Putrus	26	Golch
31	Dreggh	31	Bulgroth
32	Festrach	32	Spatterblight
33	Usghul	33	Sphek
34	Viluthrox	34	Seep
35	Htholgh	35	Maggotfather
36	Dolgoth	36	Gutslopp
41	Gnaxos	41	Thraxx
42	Lugorias	42	the Reviled
43	Ragthor	43	Sluthgor
44	Clattercyst	44	Blorgh
45	Fesmus	45	Squirmlung
46	Grume	46	Pustulor
51	Bulghor	51	Putrexh
52	Effulgous	52	Rotbolgh
53	Volxox	53	the Rotted
54	Vulguthrot	54	the Jovial
55	Pustus	55	the Putrid
56	Grulgux	56	the Seeping
61	D'lgoth	61	the Repugnant
62	Blothlok	62	Gwuch
63	Molgh	63	Putrughor
64	Blutherblight	64	the Vomitous
65	Feccustus	65	the Reeking
66	Putryx	66	Thrombhoxis

AGENTS OF BILE

'What unclean power burns within these aberrations? Not the dark purity of the Daemon, nor the genetic might of the Space Marine. No, this is something else, something debase and singular. I must have its secrets for myself...'

- Argento Corian

CREATIONS OF BILE

In this section you'll find rules for Battle-forged armies that include Chaos Space Marine Detachments taken from the followers of Fabius Bile. With these vile tools you can take your collection of Heretic Astartes and twist it into something altogether more foul and terrible.

The rules presented in this section are intended to be used in addition to those presented in *Codex: Chaos Space Marines*.

This section contains an updated datasheet for Fabius Bile that replaces the one found in *Codex: Chaos Space Marines*, and rules for fielding Detachments of his creations. You will also find additional Relics and Stratagems that can be used with these Detachments.

KEYWORDS

If Fabius Bile is your Warlord, units from your army can replace their <Legion> keyword with CREATIONS OF BILE. Note that you cannot replace the <Legion> keyword with CREATIONS OF BILE unless Fabius Bile is your Warlord.

ABILITIES

Units in CREATIONS OF BILE Detachments gain the following abilities:

THE SPIDER'S WEB

If your army is Battle-forged, all Troops units in CREATIONS OF BILE Detachments gain this ability. Such a unit that is within range of an objective marker controls it even if there are more enemy models within range of it. If an enemy unit within range of the objective marker has a similar ability, then it is controlled by the player who has the most models within range as normal.

CREATIONS OF BILE LEGION TRAIT

If your army is Battle-forged, all CHARACTER, INFANTRY (excluding CHAOS CULTIST units), BIKER and HELBRUTE units in a CREATIONS OF BILE Detachment gain the Legion Trait below.

Note that, as per the Shadowy Allies rule in *Codex: Chaos Space Marines*, Fabius Bile himself – as well as FALLEN units – cannot benefit from the Experimental Enhancements Legion Trait.

Experimental Enhancements

All of Fabius Bile's Terata are chemically and physically altered by his experiments, elevating their abilities above those of similar beings – for now...

Add 1 to the Movement and Strength characteristics of models in units with this Legion Trait.

FABIUS BILE

Clonefather. Primogenitor. Spider. Fabius Bile has laboured under many epithets during his long and wicked life, but none truly convey the unrepentant evil of this heretic crypto-scientist. A twister of flesh and a sculptor of nightmares, Fabius Bile is one of the most abominable renegades to blight the Emperor's realm.

Fabius Bile is accursed throughout the galaxy. Formerly an Apothecary of the Emperor's Children, amidst the carnage of the Horus Heresy Bile aided his Legion in their journey into the embrace of the Chaos God Slaanesh. He altered their brain chemistry to sharpen their senses, tainted their bodies with xeno-surgery and connected their pleasure centres directly to their nervous systems so that every stimulus would bring them unholy joy. As Terra burned in the fires of Horus' final, doomed assault, Bile departed the Throneworld with a hand-picked cadre of altered servants, decrying the traitors' goals as prosaic and short-sighted and earning the eternal ire of his Daemon Primarch Fulgrim in the process.

Bile moved through the war-torn Imperium, selling his services to rebel commanders for prisoners, genetic samples and ancient technologies. Yet as their warriors degenerated into ravening monsters and their worlds burned in the fires of genetic apocalypse, Bile's customers came to rue the day they struck a daemon's bargain with the Spider. Eventually, Fabius Bile found his way to the Eye of Terror. There, he offered his services to the highest bidders. He set up a new base upon the benighted crone world of Urum and transformed it into a nightmarish realm of twisted horrors.

The shattered Traitor Legions who make their home in the Eye of Terror have particular need of Bile's skills. His augmented warriors and bio-magicks can give a warband a vital edge, yet it is the skills he learned as an Apothecary that are most precious. The Traitor Legions need to extract the progenoid glands of the fallen in order to create new Chaos Space Marines and – while he is far from alone in being able to perform the requisite surgery – Bile is pre-eminent in this art.

There are some who have accused Fabius Bile of hiding always behind his armies of altered soldiers, but they are dangerously foolish. Bile is a surgically skilled warrior who has augmented his already post-human biology with the very finest results of his experimentations. In one hand he wields the Rod of Torment, which causes sanity-blasting agony with the slightest wound, and in the other the gruesomely poisonous Xyclos Needler. Meanwhile, upon his back Bile bears the Chirurgeon, a mechanical harness of spidery limbs and life-preserving hypodermics which serves to heal its master's wounds as swiftly as his foes can inflict them.

FABIUS BILE

NAME	M	WS	BS	S	T	W	A	Ld	Sv
Fabius Bile	6"	2+	3+	4	4	5	4	9	3+
Surgeon Acolyte	6"	5+	5+	3	4	1	1	6	6+

Fabius Bile is a single model equipped with: Xyclos Needler; the Chirurgeon; Rod of Torment; frag grenades; krak grenades. He can be accompanied by up to 1 Surgeon Acolyte. A Surgeon Acolyte is equipped with: Surgeon Acolyte's tools. You can only include one of this unit in your army.

WEAPON	RANGE	TYPE	S	AP	D	ABILITIES
Xyclos Needler	18"	Pistol 3	2	-2	2	Attacks made with this weapon wound on a 2+ unless the target is a VEHICLE or TITANIC unit.
Rod of Torment	Melee	Melee	+1	-1	D3	When resolving an attack made with this weapon against a VEHICLE unit, it has a Damage characteristic of 1.
Surgeon Acolyte's tools	Melee	Melee	User	-1	1	-
The Chirurgeon	Melee	Melee	4	-2	1	When the bearer fights it can make 3 additional attacks with this weapon.
Frag grenades	6"	Grenade D6	3	0	1	-
Krak grenades	6"	Grenade 1	6	-1	D3	-

ABILITIES	
	Death to the False Emperor (see *Codex: Chaos Space Marines*)

Another Pair of Hands: If Fabius Bile is accompanied by a Surgeon Acolyte, after rolling the D3 for the Enhanced Warriors ability, you can add or subtract 1 to that roll result (e.g. a D3 roll result of 3 could be a roll result of 2 or 3). If a Surgeon Acolyte is destroyed, it is ignored for the purposes of Morale tests.

The Chirurgeon: When Fabius Bile would lose a wound, roll one D6; on a 5+ that wound is not lost. In addition, at the start of each of your turns Fabius Bile regains D3 lost wounds.

Enhanced Warriors: At the end of your Movement phase, you can select one **HERETIC ASTARTES INFANTRY** unit from your army that is not a **CHARACTER** that is wholly within 6" of this unit. You cannot select a unit that has already been affected by this ability in this battle. If you do so, roll one D6; on a 1, one model from the selected unit is destroyed. Then, roll one D3 and consult the table below: |

D3	ENHANCEMENT
1	Add 1 to the Strength characteristic of models in that unit until the end of the battle.
2	Add 1 to the Toughness characteristic of models in that unit until the end of the battle.
3	Add 1 to the Attacks characteristic of models in that unit until the end of the battle.

FACTION KEYWORDS	CHAOS, HERETIC ASTARTES, CREATIONS OF BILE
KEYWORDS (FABIUS BILE)	**CHARACTER, INFANTRY, FABIUS BILE**
KEYWORDS (SURGEON ACOLYTE)	**CHARACTER, INFANTRY, SURGEON ACOLYTE**

POINTS VALUES

UNIT	MODELS PER UNIT	POINTS PER MODEL (Including wargear)
Fabius Bile	1	85
- Surgeon Acolyte	0-1	5

RELICS OF BILE

Over the millennia, Fabius Bile has amassed countless arcane treasures and twisted weapons – some of his own cunning artefice – with which to gift his favoured creations. These foul devices are precious to Bile, and their use often proves to be an integral part of his latest twisted experiments.

If Fabius Bile is your Warlord, you can give one of the following Artefacts of Chaos to a **CREATIONS OF BILE CHARACTER** model from your army, instead of other Artefacts of Chaos presented elsewhere. Named characters, such as Fabius Bile, already have one or more artefacts, and cannot be given any of these artefacts. Note that some Relics are weapons that replace one of the model's existing weapons. Where this is the case, you must, if you are using points values, still pay the cost of the weapon that is being replaced. Write down any Artefacts of Chaos your models have on your army roster.

HELM OF ALL-SEEING

This baroque helm sports an array of additional sensors, allowing the wearer to take in a tremendous amount of battlefield information in a short space of time – providing, of course, they have the requisite additional sensory organs to process it…

Whilst a model with this Relic is on the battlefield, you can roll one D6 for each Command Point you spend to use a Stratagem; on a 5+ that Command Point is refunded.

HYPER-GROWTH BOLTS

These rounds contain small amounts of Bile's most unstable growth-inducing concoctions. When introduced into the bloodstream, armour splits as the victim's musculature rapidly swells before collapsing under its own weight.

When you give a model this Relic, select one bolt pistol, boltgun or combi-weapon (see *Codex: Chaos Space Marines* wargear lists) that model is equipped with. When a model with this Relic shoots with that weapon, you can choose for it to fire a Hyper-growth bolt. If you do, you can only make one attack with that weapon, but that attack always wounds on a 2+ (unless the target is a **VEHICLE** unit) and has a Damage characteristic of 4.

LIVING CARAPACE

This living armour moves seamlessly in concert with its wearer. With a thought, the wearer can secrete growth hormones into these plates, thickening them, repairing damaged sections and making them nigh invulnerable.

At the start of your turn, a model with this Relic regains 1 lost wound. In addition, when resolving an attack against this model, add 1 to the saving throw (invulnerable saves are unaffected).

CREATIONS OF BILE STRATAGEMS

If your army is Battle-forged and includes any **CREATIONS OF BILE** Detachments (excluding Auxiliary Support Detachments), you have access to the Stratagems shown below and on the following page, meaning you can spend Command Points to activate them. These help to reflect the unique strategies used by Bile's warriors on the battlefield.

1CP

VENOMOUS CLAWS
Creations of Bile Stratagem
These warriors unsheathe diamond-hard envenomed claws from their fingertips, ready to rend and tear the foe.

Use this Stratagem in the Fight phase when you select a **CREATIONS OF BILE** unit (excluding **CHAOS CULTISTS**) to fight. Until the end of that phase, when resolving an attack made with the close combat weapon profile by a model in that unit, an unmodified hit roll of 6 automatically scores a hit and successfully wounds the target (do not make a wound roll).

1CP

MONSTROUS VISAGES
Creations of Bile Stratagem
Bile's experimental ministrations have left these warriors as freakish monsters. Cursed with clusters of compound eyes, distended, fang-stuffed jaws or myriad other grotesqueries, they are hideous to behold.

Use this Stratagem at the start of any phase. Select one **CREATIONS OF BILE INFANTRY** unit from your army (excluding **CHAOS CULTISTS**). Until the end of the turn, when resolving an attack made by an enemy model within 6" of that unit, subtract 1 from the hit roll.

MACROTENSILE SINEWS

1CP

Creations of Bile Stratagem

Injecting auto-stimulants into their enhanced muscles, these warriors leap and bound across the battlefield.

Use this Stratagem at the start of your Movement phase. Select one **Creations of Bile Infantry** unit (excluding **Chaos Cultists**) from your army. Until the end of the turn this unit can be chosen to charge with even if they Advanced this turn and when an Advance or charge roll is made for this unit, add 1 to the result.

THE MASTER IS WATCHING

1CP

Creations of Bile Stratagem

Feeling Bile's expectant gaze from across the battlefield, his enhanced warriors strive slavishly to impress.

Use this Stratagem in your Shooting phase or the Fight phase, when a **Creations of Bile Infantry** unit from your army (excluding **Chaos Cultists**) that is visible to and within 12" of your Warlord is chosen to shoot or fight with. Until the end of that phase, when resolving an attack made by a model in that unit, you can re-roll the hit roll.

DERMAL CHITINATION

1CP

Creations of Bile Stratagem

These fighters secrete a hardening resin through their skin, temporarily toughening their already resilient hides.

Use this Stratagem in your opponent's Shooting phase when a **Creations of Bile Infantry** unit from your army (excluding **Chaos Cultists**) is selected as the target of any attacks. Add 1 to that unit's Toughness characteristic until the end of that phase.

TAKEN ALIVE

1CP

Creations of Bile Stratagem

To be snatched away by Fabius Bile and his creations for experimentation is an altogether nightmarish fate.

Use this Stratagem in the Fight phase when a model from an enemy unit is destroyed as the result of an attack made with a melee weapon by a model from a **Creations of Bile Infantry** unit from your army. For the rest of the battle, when taking a Morale test for that enemy model's unit, each model in that unit that was destroyed that turn is treated as two models for the purposes of taking that Morale test. Each enemy unit can only be selected for this Stratagem once.

SUPREME CREATION

1CP

Creations of Bile Stratagem

This warrior was already a dark champion of Chaos. Now, he is both more and less – monstrously powerful but yoked utterly to Fabius Bile's will.

Use this Stratagem before the battle. Choose one **Creations of Bile Character** model from your army that is not Fabius Bile. You can give that model one of the abilities from those listed below. You can only use this Stratagem once per battle.

Prime Test Subject

Whilst Bile has unlocked a portion of the mysterious bio-alchemy used in the creation of the warriors of the Adeptus Custodes, only the strongest test subjects survive the rampant cell transformations.

Add 1 to the Strength and Toughness characteristics of this model.

The Master's Hound

With enhanced sensory and aggressive instincts, this practically mindless creature is used by Bile to hunt down those he wishes to conduct further research upon.

Add 1 to Advance and charge rolls for this model. In addition, if this model made a charge move, was charged or performed a Heroic Intervention, add 1 to the model's Attacks characteristic until the end of the turn.

Ravenous Biology

Through a quirk of chemistry, this creation's cells repair at a tremendous rate, but require constant fuelling. This can only be achieved by devouring the flesh of their foes to satiate their physiology.

When this model would lose a wound, roll one D6; on a 6, that wound is not lost. In addition, at the end of the Fight phase, this model regains D3 lost wounds if any enemy models were destroyed within 1" of them this phase.